FIBRE REINFORCED
MATERIALS

BRE Building Research Series   Volume 2

Practical Studies from the Building Research Establishment

FIBRE REINFORCED MATERIALS

THE CONSTRUCTION PRESS

LANCASTER   LONDON   NEW YORK·

The Construction Press Ltd,
Lancaster, England.

A subsidiary company of Longman Group Ltd, London.
Associated companies, branches and representatives
throughout the world.

Published in the United States of America by
Longman Inc, New York.

First published 1978

D
624.18
BUI

ISBN 0 904406 38 5

Printed in Great Britain at The Pitman Press, Bath

Preface

This book and its companion volumes bring together in a bound and edited form research papers originating from the British Building Research Establishment (BRE) and originally issued singly in a series of Current Papers. Until now this rich source of information has never been collated and published in traditional bound format and in consequence many potential readers have not been aware of, or had ready access to, the valuable data contained in the series.

These volumes do not contain every paper relating to each subject that has ever been issued by the BRE. To have included them all would have resulted in unmanageable volumes of enormous size! More importantly, to have included them all would have meant preserving in a permanent reference format for an international readership many papers which were intended to be of relevance only to a local British readership or which, important though they were at the time, are not of lasting significance.

The volumes have therefore been carefully compiled so as to contain all those papers which are considered to be of long-term value and genuine international interest issued during the five year span 1973-1978. As such they are permanent, convenient and practical reference works which will be well used by both research workers and building practitioners. Each volume has been carefully subject indexed and, for the benefit of Overseas readers, the contents are published in French, German and Spanish as well as English.

ACKNOWLEDGEMENT

We have pleasure in acknowledging the co-operation of both the Building Research Establishment and Her Majesty's Stationery Office in granting us permission to publish the Current Papers in this volume.

Contents

Table des matières

Inhaltsverzeichnis

Table de materias

Glass-reinforced polyesters

Prediction of thermal conductivity of GRP laminates (CP 70/76)

K. Maries

NOMENCLATURE
Symbols

a,b see equation (2)

B see equation (10)

k thermal conductivity

s packing factor; see equation (6)

V volume fraction

v porosity volume fraction

W weight

a see equation (7)

β pore shape factor; see equation (1)

ρ density

θ angle of heat flow to perpendicular; see equation (14)

Subscripts

g glass reinforcement

ℓ laminate

r resin

The prediction of thermal conductivity in GRP laminates from five theoretical models are compared with the experimental results for five different types of glass reinforcement. One model is shown to predict values within ± 3 per cent of experimental data for all the samples except for non-planar, chopped strand, reinforcement, where the prediction was low.

FOREWORD

A study of the burning and thermal decomposition of plastics materials has been carried out by the QMC Industrial Research Ltd under a contract placed by the Fire Research Station. An important part of this study has been the development of a heat transfer model to describe the decomposition behaviour of composite materials containing plastics. A reasonable estimate of the thermal conductivity of such composites is required for this model.

This paper reports that part of the study on the prediction of the thermal conductivity of composites, in this case glass fibre reinforced polyesters (GRPs), from the thermal conductivity of their constituents. Values of thermal conductivity obtained by the proposed method are not only applicable to decomposition studies, but should also be of value wherever the thermal conductivity of a composite material is required.

A complete account of the studies under the contract is to be published elsewhere, enquiries about which should be addressed to the Fire Research Station.

INTRODUCTION

Glass fibre reinforced polyester resin (GRPs) are well established as building materials, but in addition to the intended improvement of the mechanical properties of the resin, the reinforcement has significant effects on the thermal behaviour of the composite material. During development of a computer model[1] to analyse the thermal behaviour of GRP in fire environments, it was necessary to establish the thermal properties of a variety of GRP laminates. Such data, however, have a wider application.

Although the specific heat of a laminate is simply the volume-weighted sum of the specific heats of the constituents, the determination of the thermal conductivity of a laminate from those of its constituents is more complex. The investigation reported here suggests that the thermal conductivity of GRP at temperatures below that at which decomposition of the resin occurs can be accurately predicted, without resorting to special experiments, from a knowledge of the conductivities of the constituents and their geometrical arrangement.

Glass reinforcements can be broadly classified into four types — chopped strand mat, woven cloth, woven rovings, and dispersions of short fibres. The many models developed to describe the thermal conductivity of isotropic two-phase mixtures are in general not suitable for GRP because even in the case of dispersed glass fibres, these are rarely randonly orientated, so that conductivity is still highly anisotropic.

MODELS FOR THERMAL CONDUCTIVITY OF LAMINATES

An exact mathematical treatment of GRP thermal conductivity would require knowledge of the position of each individual fibre. Therefore most models are simplified according to the following assumptions:

(i)   The reinforcement is evenly dispersed in the resin.

(ii)   The resin and glass are thermally isotropic.

(iii)   Thermal contact resistance between resin and glass is negligibly low.

(iv)   Twisting of fibre bundles is ignored.

Most GRP laminates contain air inclusions resulting from the lay-up process, which can occur both in the resin (porosity) and inside or around the fibre bundles. If it is assumed that the pores are spherical and evenly distributed in the resin, then this feature can be accounted for by the dilute porous dispersion theory[2] developed from the exact Maxwell solutions for spherical dispersions:

$$\frac{k}{k_r} = \frac{1-v}{1+\beta v} \qquad \qquad \dots \text{(1)}$$

Other factors, such as differences in weft and warp reinforcement, and the effects of bundle compression at cross-over points, have been found to have only marginal effects on thermal conductivity[3,4], and will not be considered further here.

Five models of thermal conductivity are examined here, with calculations based on the assumption of one-dimensional heat flow perpendicular to the plane of reinforcement.

Model I (Knappe and Martinez-Freire[4])

The approach used in this model is to consider a unit volume cube of laminate, and group the fibre reinforcement into two solid prisms which correspond to the warp and weft directions (see Figure 1). Then, from the assumptions listed above, it can be shown that the laminate conductivity is given by:

$$k_\ell = \frac{ab}{\dfrac{a+b}{k_g} + \dfrac{1-(a+b)}{k_r}} + \frac{b(1-a)}{\dfrac{b}{k_g} + \dfrac{1-b}{k_r}} + \frac{a(1-b)}{\dfrac{a}{k_g} + \dfrac{1-a}{k_r}} + (1-a)(1-b)\,k_r \qquad \ldots\,(2)$$

a and b are the sides of the square cross-section prisms in each direction, so that differing amounts of fibre reinforcement in the warp and weft directions can be allowed for.

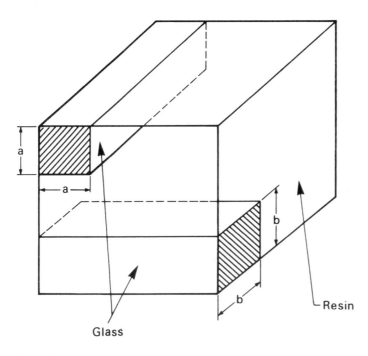

Figure 1 Cube model (see reference 4)

Model II (Shlenskii[5])

In this model, the fibres are considered to be arranged in a one-directional array, spaced in either a cubic or hexagonal fashion and surrounded or impregnated with resin (see Figure 2). First of all, a value of thermal conductivity k' is calculated for the case where the fibres touch. For the two types of array, these equations are:

Model IIA (cubic packing)

$$\frac{k'}{k_r} = \frac{(k_g/k_r - 1)}{\dfrac{\pi}{2} - \dfrac{2}{\sqrt{(k_g/k_r - 1)^2 - 1}}\,.\tanh^{-1}\sqrt{1 - 2\,k_r/k_g}} \qquad \ldots\,(3)$$

Model IIB (hexagonal packing)

$$\frac{k'}{k_r} = \frac{1}{\dfrac{0.866}{k''/k_r} + \dfrac{0.134}{k_g/k_r}} \qquad \ldots\,(4)$$

5

where

$$\frac{k''}{k_r} = \frac{0.732 \, (k_g/k_r - 1)}{0.824 - \dfrac{0.870}{\sqrt{(k_g/k_r - 1)^2 - 1}} \cdot \tanh^{-1}\sqrt{1 - 2 \, k_r/k_g}} \qquad \ldots (5)$$

Then the laminate thermal conductivity k_ℓ is calculated assuming that the fibres are uniformly spaced and surrounded by resin:

$$\frac{k_\ell}{k_r} = \frac{(1 + s) \, (k'/k_r + s)}{(1 + s) + s \, (k'/k_r + s)} \qquad \ldots (6)$$

where the packing factor

$$s = a\sqrt{\frac{\rho_g \, (1 + v) - \rho_r}{\rho \, (1 + v) - \rho_r}} - 1 \qquad \ldots (7)$$

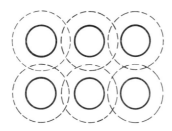

Model 11A: resin impregnated cubic array

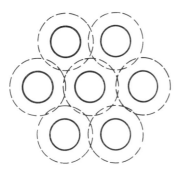

Model 11B: resin impregnated hexagonal array

Figure 2 Fibre packing arrangements (after Shlenskii [5])

Model III (Clayton[3])
A number of equations were considered by Clayton for describing thermal conductivity perpendicular to the reinforcement plane, and the most successful was:

$$\sqrt{\frac{k_\ell}{k_r}} = \frac{\sqrt{(1 - V_g)^2 \, (k_g/k_r - 1)^2 + 4 \, k_g/k_r} - (1 - V_g) \, (k_g/k_r - 1)}{2} \qquad \ldots (8)$$

Model IV (Springer and Tsai[6])

This model makes use of the analogy between mechanical shear loading and heat transfer, where the calculation of elastic modulus in a composite may be considered equivalent to thermal conductivity (as well as other properties such as dielectric constant and magnetic permeability). For a cubic packing array (see Model IIA above):

$$\frac{k_\ell}{k_r} = 1 - \sqrt{V_g} + \frac{1}{\sqrt{\dfrac{1}{V_g} + \dfrac{B}{2}}} \qquad \dots (9)$$

where

$$B = 2\left(\frac{k_r}{k_g} - 1\right) \qquad \dots (10)$$

EXPERIMENTS

Thermal conductivity measurements were carried out on a resin reinforced with five different arrangements of E-glass fibre. Details of the reinforcements are given in Table 1, and diagrams of the three woven materials are shown in Figure 3.

Table 1 Details of glass reinforcement

Sample Code	Type of E-glass reinforcement	nominal weight g m^{-2}	nominal thickness mm	number of threads/mm		number of layers per sample	overall sample thickness, mm
				warp	weft		
A	chopped strand mat (Multemat)	450	—	—	—	4	3.35
B	plain weave fabric (type Y360)	186	0.15	1.42	1.26	14	3.30
C	8-end satin weave fabric (type Y403)	305	0.20	2.24	2.13	8	3.45
D	woven rovings (type Y702)	770	0.69	3.20	3.20	4	3.35
E	chopped rovings	—	—	—	—	—	7.62
F	plain resin	—	—	—	—	—	3.30

E-glass density : 2.5 kg m^{-3}

thermal conductivity : 1.035 W m^{-1} K^{-1}

Sample preparation

Careful preparation of the samples was necessary to ensure that the distribution of reinforcement in the resin was as even as possible, and that air inclusions were reduced to a minimum.

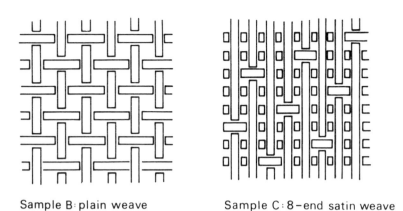

Sample B: plain weave   Sample C: 8-end satin weave

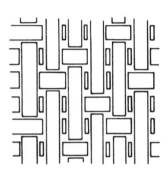

Sample D: woven rovings

Figure 3 Weave construction of glass fabric reinforcements

The resin was catalysed immediately before use with just enough catalyst to allow sufficient time to lay up the laminates before gelation occurred. Each layer of reinforcement was stippled by brush until completely wet by the resin, and the completed laminate was squeegeed to remove trapped air. 3 mm spacers were placed round the edges, and pressure applied to consolidate the laminate during cure which was at room temperature. Subsequent viewing under a microscope of sectioned, polished samples showed good wetting, few voids and uniform spacing of the reinforcement.

Sample analysis

The weight fraction of glass, W_g, was determined by measuring the weight of materials remaining after the resin had been burnt off, making allowance for the charred resin residue which was determined in a separate experiment on the resin alone. The density p_ℓ of the laminate was measured by the water suspension method, from which the proportional volume contents of glass, resin and voids were calculated:

$$V_g = \frac{\rho_\ell \cdot W_g}{\rho_g} \qquad \qquad \dots (11)$$

$$V_r = \frac{\rho_\ell \cdot W_r}{\rho_r} \qquad \qquad \dots (12)$$

$$v = 1 - (V_g + V_r) \qquad \qquad \dots (13)$$

These parameters were determined for insertion in the models described above, and the results for each of the samples are given in Table 2.

Table 2 Weight and volume analysis of GRP samples

Sample	Weight analysis			Volume analysis		
	Laminate specific gravity ρ_ℓ	Glass fraction W_g	Resin fraction W_r	Glass fraction V_g	Resin fraction V_r	Resin porosity fraction v
A	1.74	0.345	0.655	0.2401	0.7306	0.0293
B	1.84	0.424	0.576	0.3121	0.6793	0.0086
C	1.80	0.372	0.628	0.2678	0.7246	0.0076
D	1.86	0.457	0.543	0.3400	0.6474	0.0126
E	1.83	0.423	0.577	0.3096	0.6769	0.0135
F	1.56	–	1.0	–	1.0	–

Measurement of thermal conductivity

A double-sided hot-plate apparatus (Figure 4) was used to determine thermal conductivity at mean temperatures of 20°C and 55°C. A temperature difference of 10°C was maintained across each sample, but since conductivity of the samples varied little with temperature, this was considered to be of no importance. The experimental error of the method was estimated as ± 3 per cent.

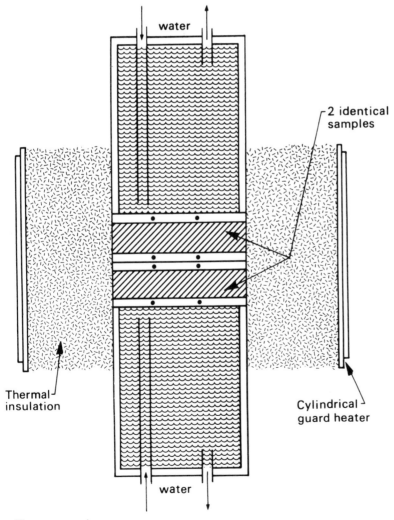

• Thermocouples

Figure 4 Thermal conductivity apparatus

9

DISCUSSION

The experimental results and the predictions from the 5 models are compared in Table 3. Model I gives the most consistently accurate predictions, within −3 to +3 per cent for samples A to D, which is of the same magnitude as the experimental error. The two versions of Model II are hardly distinguishable, but give predictions up to 15 per cent higher than experimental values.

Table 3 Comparison of theoretical and experimental determinations of GRP thermal conductivity

| Sample | Temperature °C | Experimental values | Thermal conductivity, Wm^{-1} K^{-1} Values predicted by models | | | | |
			I	II A	II B	III	IV
A	15/25	0.24	0.244	0.278	0.280	0.260	0.242
	50/60	0.25	0.255	0.289	0.292	0.271	0.253
B	15/25	0.28	0.284	0.322	0.324	0.300	0.276
	50/60	0.29	0.296	0.335	0.337	0.311	0.281
C	15/25	0.27	0.262	0.302	0.302	0.279	0.259
	50/60	0.28	0.274	0.314	0.317	0.291	0.271
D	15/25	0.31	0.299	0.334	0.335	0.311	0.286
	50/60	0.32	0.311	0.346	0.348	0.323	0.299
E	15/25	0.30	0.281	0.318	0.320	0.296	0.273
	50/60	0.32	0.293	0.330	0.333	0.308	0.286
	15/25	(see	0.286	0.322	0.324	0.301	0.279
	50/60	section 4)	0.299	0.334	0.337	0.313	0.291
F	15/25	0.19	–	–	–	–	–
	50/60	0.20	–	–	–	–	–

In the case of sample E (chopped strand reinforcement), all models predict values differing from experiment. However, all the models assume that the fibre reinforcement is perpendicular to the direction of heat flow, whereas the unsuccessful attempt to produce random fibre orientation resulted in a dispersion of up to 15° from the plane of the samples. Clayton[3] suggests the following equation to calculate non-perpendicular thermal conductivity at an angle θ:

$$k_{\theta} \quad = \quad k_{\perp}\left[1 + \left(\frac{k_{/\!/}}{k} - 1\right)\sin^2\theta\right] \qquad \qquad \dots (14)$$

where $\perp$ refers to the direction perpendicular to the reinforcement plane

$/\!/$ refers to the direction parallel to the reinforcement plane

$k/\!/$ is calculated from a simple Ohm's law type expression[4]:

$$k_{/\!/} = V_g k_g + V_r k_r \qquad \qquad \dots (15)$$

This equation has been used to adjust the value for sample E predicted by the five models, adopting a mean deviation of 7.5°. The adjusted values are shown in Table 3. Note that Model I still predicts values some 6 per cent different from experimental results.

CONCLUSIONS
Within the limited range of GRP samples examined by these experiments, equation (2) has been shown to give acceptably accurate predictions of GRP laminate thermal conductivity. Having measured thermal conductivity for a specific formulation of resin, the composite conductivity value can be predicted without resort to further time-consuming experiments by using the glass reinforcement data normally available from manufacturers.

Although this information was generated for use in computer model studies of fire behaviour of GRP, it is equally valuable for any situation, such as determination of U values, where thermal conductivity must be determined.

REFERENCES
1 Calcraft, **A M** and **Maries, K.** Plastics and Polymers. 1974. **42**, (162) 247.

2 **Belle, J** and **Berman, R M, AEC REs.** Dev Rpt, WAPD — TM — 586, 1967.

3 **Clayton, W A.** AIAA Paper No 71—380, 1971.

4 **Knappe, W** and **Martinez-Freire, P.** Kunstoffe, 1965, **55**, 776.

5 **Shlenskii, O F.** Sov Plast, 1966, **12**, 35.

6 **Springer, G S** and **Tsai, S W.** J Compos Mater, 1967, 1, 166.

The weathering of glass-reinforced polyesters under stress — short-term behaviour (CP 56/76)

J.F. Norris, J.R. Crowder and C. Probert

Glass reinforced plastics (grp) have been used in building for some 20 years. Originally introduced in the form of translucent corrugated sheeting intended primarily as rooflighting, grp has since achieved a wider use as opaque cladding for buildings.[1] However, in only a few instances [2-4] have grp components for either function been designed to utilise more than a very small proportion of the short term strength of the material.

One reason for this is the lack of rigidity in grp; in designing to achieve adequate stiffness, other stresses have been incurred only at low levels. A second reason is that the long term behaviour of the material is uncertain, and, in particular, its strength after long periods in use is unknown. The number of designs in which grp fulfils a structural or semi-structural role is increasing, but the rate of increase will be constrained unless the material can be used efficiently, and this will only come about with the availability of accurate design data relating to long term strength.[5]

Towards this end, a preliminary trial has recently been carried out at the Building Research Station.[6] Dumb-bell shaped specimens of polyester laminates reinforced with chopped strand glass mat were exposed to the weather under a tensile stress approximately 25% of their ultimate tensile strength (uts). Sets of specimens were withdrawn after various periods of exposure and their residual strengths were determined. Chopped strand mat is a highly variable material and the properties of laminates incorporating this form of reinforcement show a corresponding scatter. Because of practical difficulties encountered in preparing the large number of specimens required, the results of the preliminary trial were useful only in providing guidelines for future trials. No doubt for the same reasons, other workers have done little along these lines.

For many years, the long term weathering behaviour of plastics, including reinforced plastics, has been studied at BRS,[7] but in these and other exposure trials,[8-10] and also in accelerated weathering studies,[9-11] specimens were subjected to no external stress. Other workers have studied the long term behaviour of unstressed specimens in water, chemical and thermal environments,[12-14] and the effect of considerable stress on reinforced plastics in controlled laboratory environments [15-19] or under rather extreme conditions.[18-21] These studies have shown that the combination of adverse environment and simultaneous stress has a particularly detrimental effect on grp.

The few studies that have been made of the combined effects of weather and stress have tended to concentrate on the creep properties of the material rather than its residual strength,[22] or the form of applied stress has been unconventional [23] or inappropriate for design purposes.[24] Barrett and Steel [24] showed that reinforced polyester samples could sustain for a year no more than 20% of their short term ultimate stress when exposed under flexural loads at

tropical sites in Australia, although similar epoxide laminates could sustain up to 48% of their short term strength under the same conditions. Zilvar [22] also chose flexural loading to study the influence of natural weathering on the creep behaviour of grp and found a significant increase over the creep rate observed under laboratory conditions.

However, while flexural properties may serve as a means of following the deterioration of the resin, flexural data are not normally used for design purposes with grp. Flexural values are not absolute for the material but depend to a much greater extent on the dimensions of the specimen under test than do tensile values. As the provision of design data was the main aim of this work, specimens were exposed to the weather under a tensile stress because resin degradation was believed to be more severe under such a loading. But while tensile testing procedures produce more widely applicable design data, the tensile strength of grp is primarily related to the glass reinforcement and is likely to be rather insensitive to changes in the resin. A secondary objective was to investigate the mechanism of strength loss and failure, in which resin degradation would be expected to play a prominent role. Accordingly, both flexural and tensile short term tests were performed on specimens after exposure.

EXPERIMENTAL DETAILS

Only brief experimental details are given here. Full details and the reasoning behind the decisions involved have been recorded elsewhere.[25]

Laminate fabrication

Two resin systems typical of those used at present for building panels [26] were selected:

A Crystic 345PA (Class 1 Resin*)/Crystic Gelcoat 65LS (general purpose isophthalic resin)

B Crystic 326 (Class 2 Resin*)/Crystic Gelcoat 46PA (filled, flame retardant resin).

Catalyst M (medium activity MEKP) was used for all resins. From both resin systems, laminates were constructed with two gelcoats, each nominally 0.46 mm thick, separated by a reinforced layer of 1.9 mm nominal thickness. All laminates were reinforced with two layers of 450 g m^{-2} Fibreglass SuprEmat chopped strand glass fibre mat. The volume fraction of glass (V_f) in the core of the laminates was approximately 0.22; in the complete laminate including gelcoats the V_f was 0.16. Before demoulding, laminates were cured at room temperature for 21 hours and then postcured in an oven for 3 hours at 80°C.

---

*Surface spread of flame classification as defined in BS 476:1971, Part 7. Both systems achieve a Class II rating overall.

Table 1. Exposure programme format

Resin system	B — Crystic 326/Crystic 46PA				A — Crystic 345PA/Crystic 65LS			
	I		II		III		IV	
Laminate series mat orientation*	Lateral		Longitu-dinal		Lateral		Longitu-dinal	
Sub-programme number	1	2	3	4	5	6	7	8
Applied load (% uts)	25	20	0	25	25	20	0	25
Number of exposure periods	10	5	10	5	10	5	10	5
Number of specimens per set	10	10	10	10	10	10	10	10
Number of sets per period†	3	3	3	3	3	3	3	3
Number of specimens in sub-programme	300	150	300	150	300	150	300	150
Total number of specimens								1 800

* Lateral orientation: the width direction of the roll of glass mat lies along the length of the specimen
  Longitudinal orientation: the length direction of the roll of glass mat lies along the length of the specimen

† Outdoors, laboratory and control

Laminates, 762 mm x 533 mm, were fabricated to a high standard of uniformity by a method used previously [6] but since modified to incorporate refinements devised by Howe.[27] The method is described in detail elsewhere.[28]

Specimen dimensions and preparation

Because specimens of this shape could be produced fairly rapidly, a straight-sided rectangular shape, 356 mm long and 12.7 mm wide, was adopted for exposure specimens. Laminate sheets were cut by bandsaw into strips which were then reduced to the required width by milling both edges in turn. After exposure, a 25 mm length at each end of a specimen (see section on equipment design and use) was removed and the remainder of the specimen divided to give a 76 mm flexural specimen [29] and a 230 mm tensile specimen. Because they induced premature failure in a large proportion of trial specimens, the end pieces recommended for a similar British Standard tensile specimen type [29] were not used here. Analysis of the testing of control specimens [30] endorses the suitability of specimens without endgrips and of the narrower width adopted.

Exposure programme design

The total exposure programme consists of eight sub-programmes which are defined in Table 1. In sub-programmes 2, 4, 6 and 8, sets of specimens were withdrawn after 1, 4, 16, 64 and 256 weeks' exposure; in sub-programmes 1, 3, 5 and 7, which incorporate the principal exposure conditions, additional sets were withdrawn after 2, 8, 32, 128 and 512 weeks, giving a total of 10 exposure periods. Each set comprised 10 specimen triplets. The centre specimen from each triplet served as a control specimen in the manner suggested by Owen and Howe,[17] and one of the outer specimens was exposed outdoors under the appropriate load. The remaining specimen in each triplet was subjected to the same load for an equal period in a temperature and humidity controlled laboratory environment.

Specimen triplets were randomised before being assigned to an appropriate sub-programme. Randomisation procedures were also used to differentiate between laboratory and outdoor exposure specimens in each triplet and to determine from which end of the larger specimen the tensile and flexural specimens should be cut.

Equipment design and use

Stressed specimens were exposed on the weathering site on racks (Fig.1) which could hold 10 independently stressed specimen chains. A specimen chain (Fig.3) consisted of two specimens linked in series by stainless steel clamping plates. The use of a jig in the clamping operation ensured that the specimen chain was linear. The required dead loading was applied to the chain by a wire passing over a pulley, and the anchor bar was then locked in the extended position. The applied load was maintained by springs and checked periodically. As expected,[31] no relaxation has been observed except during the first week's exposure.

Unstressed specimens were attached to wooden frames in a manner which permitted thermal movement. All outdoor exposed specimens were inclined at 45°C facing south during exposure. Laboratory specimens were held vertically while under stress, which was applied in a similar manner to that on the outdoor specimens (Fig.2). A set of specimens was also kept in the laboratory under no stress for eventual testing.

Specimens to remain exposed for 128 weeks or less were first exposed on 4/9/1973 (resin system B specimens) and on 2/10/1973 (resin system A specimens). All specimens to remain exposed for longer periods were first exposed on 30/10/1973.

Short term 'testing'

After tensile and flexural specimens had been cut, they were stored at 23 ± 2°C for at least 40 hours [32] before being tested on an Instron TTDM universal tensile testing machine. For tensile testing, the specimen was gripped between rubber-faced jaws tightened to a constant torque of 25 N . m, and an extensometer with a 50 mm gauge length was attached to the specimen. A jaw separation rate of 0.0833 mm s[-1] was used. Flexural testing was effected with a three-point bending jig with a 50 mm span, at a jaw separation rate of 0.167 mm s[-1]. These methods are essentially similar to those in BS 2782 [29] but differ in the number of specimens used — 10 for each determination — in the grips, and in the absence of glued end pieces on the tensile test specimens.

The point of gelcoat failure of each specimen, a clearly audible crack, was recorded during testing. This enabled five

Fig.1   Stressing racks

Fig.2   Indoor stressing racks

values to be read from each trace — the force and extension (of tensile specimens) or deflection (of flexural specimens) at gelcoat failure and at ultimate failure, and the force at 0.2 percent extension or 1.0 mm deflection. From the latter values of force and measurements of the width and thickness of each specimen, elastic moduli in tension and in flexure have been calculated, while the former values of force have enabled maximum stress values to be deduced. For tensile specimens, maximum stress values have been calculated by the traditional method, and also by the method of Ball and Raymond [33] as a force per unit width per nominal unit thickness. Deflections at failure of flexural specimens have been converted to maximum strain values. Finally, for both tensile (T) and flexural (F) specimens, the stress at gelcoat failure (gts; gfs) was calculated as a percentage of the stress at ultimate failure (uts; ufs).

RESULTS

Analysis of short term testing results of control specimens

(i) Mean tensile strengths and levels of applied stress

Before the start of an exposure sub-programme, the short term testing of all corresponding control specimens was completed, allowing the determination of the mean ultimate tensile force for specimens of each laminate series, presented in Table 2. This permitted the calculation of the forces to be applied to stressed specimens while exposed, and to the equivalent laboratory specimens.

It will be noted in Table 2 that both series of laminates fabricated with a longitudinal mat orientation (defined in Table 1) were weaker than the corresponding series of laminates with a lateral mat orientation, but the difference

Table 2. Mean ultimate tensile loads and applied loads

Laminate series	I	II	III	IV
Ultimate tensile load (kg)	259	226	278	219
Applied load: 25% utl (kg)	66	56.5	69.5	55
20% utl (kg)	53		55.5	

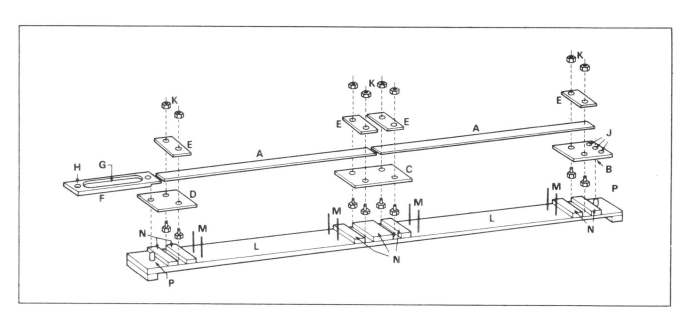

Fig.3   Specimen chain and assembly jig. Key as follows: A — specimens; B — specimen/springs connecting plate; C — specimen/specimen connecting plate; D — specimen/anchor bar connecting plate; E — clamping plates; F — anchor bar; G — clamping bolt slot; H — loading wire attachment hole; J — spring attachment holes; K — clamping bolts; L — assembly jig; M — specimen alignment pins; N — bolt head restraining plates; P — connecting plate alignment pins

is considerably greater for resin system A laminates (Series III and IV).

If the equation proposed in Reference 28, to relate the contribution of components to total strength, provides an accurate description, arguments developed from it suggest that system B makes a considerably greater contribution to a laminate's strength than does resin system A, but the resin–glass bond is correspondingly weaker in resin system B laminates. Additionally, the chopped strand mat contains at least 21% less glass in the weaker orientation.

(ii) Uniformity of laminates

Average values of properties of specimens in each laminate series are recorded in Table 3. Differences between sheets in the same series were generally not significant ($< 95\%$). Among sheet average uts values of Series I laminates, a high significance was calculated for the two greatest differences between pairs of sheets only, out of 136 values. Among equivalent values for Series II and IV laminates, no significant effect was found, while significance values for Series III laminates showed one sheet to be significantly different from the population. However as all specimens were assigned to programmes after randomisation, specimens from all sheets of each series were used.

(iii) Abnormal failures in short term tests

In short term tensile testing of specimens, the failure was considered to be abnormal if the point of failure lay within one of the testing machines' jaws ('gripbreaks') or coincided with one of the extensometer clamps ('extensometer breaks'), or if the specimens slipped suddenly within the jaws prior to ultimate failure ('slipbreaks'). All failures in which none of these three events was observed were deemed to be 'normal'. Analysis and discussion of the different failure modes, in the accompanying paper,[30] showed that the results for 'gripbreak' failures did not differ significantly from the 'normal' ones, and have been included, but the 'slipbreak' and 'extensometer breaks' were significantly different and have been excluded.

Analysis of exposure specimen results

(i) Observations of specimens while exposed

No specimens have failed prematurely while under applied stress during exposure, nor has any gelcoat cracking been found. Resin system B specimens have yellowed slightly, but no discernible change in the colour of resin system A has been observed.

(ii) Short term testing after exposure – presentation of results

Because of the high uniformity of laminates used in this study, little difference is seen between tensile strengths calculated by the traditional method and by the method of Ball and Raymond.[33] Therefore gts's and uts's calculated by the latter method only are included here, in absolute units in Fig.4 and as a percentage of the figure for the corresponding control specimen in Fig.5.

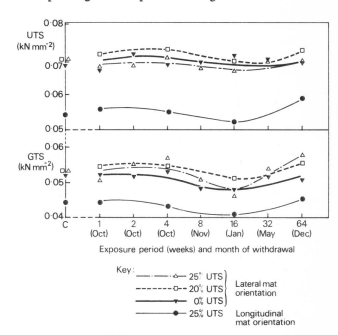

Fig.4   Gelcoat failure (gts) and ultimate tensile strengths (uts) of resin system A specimens, expressed in absolute units

Table 3. Laminate series averages

Laminate series (number of specimens)		Tensile stress (kN/mm²)	Extension (%)	Tensile stress (kN/mm²)	Extension (%)	Elastic modulus in tension (kN/mm²)	Flexural stress (kN/mm²)	Strain	Flexural stress (kN/mm²)	Strain	Elastic modulus in flexure (kN/mm²)
		At gelcoat failure		At ultimate failure			At gelcoat failure		At ultimate failure		
I (250)	av*	5.6	0.81	6.6	1.08	7.7	10.2	1.94	12.5	2.7	6.0
	C of V	8%	15%	8%	18%	5%	14%	14%	14%	11%	8%
II (50)	av	4.9	0.78	5.7	0.99	7.3	8.7	1.84	10.8	2.8	5.3
	C of V	10%	15%	8%	15%	5%	12%	14%	17%	16%	6%
III (250)	av	5.3	0.68	6.9	1.19	8.1	9.0	1.39	12.5	2.7	7.0
	C of V	9%	12%	9%	17%	4%	14%	17%	16%	15%	7%
IV (50)	av	4.4	0.63	5.5	1.02	7.5	7.0	1.12	10.9	3.1	6.6
	C of V	10%	15%	8%	20%	5%	9%	12%	15%	14%	6%
		$\times 10^{-2}$		$\times 10^{-2}$			$\times 10^{-2}$	$\times 10^{-2}$	$\times 10^{-2}$	$\times 10^{-2}$	

*av = average, C of V = coefficient of variation

15

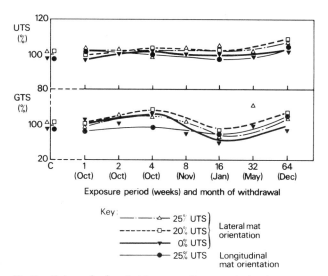

Fig.5   Gelcoat (gts) and ultimate tensile strengths (uts) of resin system A specimens, expressed as a percentage of the equivalent value of an adjacent control specimen

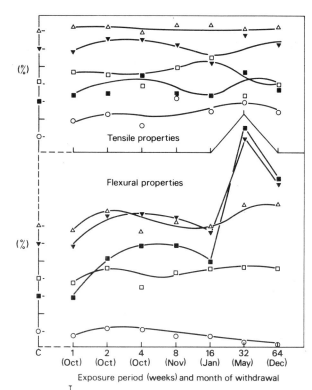

Fig.6   Properties of resin system A exposure specimens, expressed as a percentage of the equivalent value of an adjacent control specimen. The vertical scale is indicated, the first point C (= control) on each line defining 100%

Comparison of Fig.5 with Fig.4 shows that the use of control specimens in the manner suggested by Owen and Howe [17] reduces scatter appreciably so that Fig.5 immediately conveys a clearer impression of the variation of residual tensile strengths with exposure period; other properties in Fig.6 (resin system A), 7 (resin system B) and 8 (resin system A, laboratory specimens) are expressed only in this way.

(iii) Short term testing after exposure – discussion of results

The recurrent feature throughout all tensile and flexural stresses and extensions of resin system B specimens (Fig.7) is an increase in value during the first four weeks' exposure, an ensuing decline continuing until 32 weeks' exposure, and a further slight increase in the latest recorded values after 64 weeks' exposure. This behaviour is most marked in extensions at gelcoat failure, in which an initial increase of around 30% is followed by a decline of 40%; a subsequent increase of 10% gives a gelcoat failure extension after 64 weeks' exposure which is very similar to that of unexposed control specimens. Significance tests confirm the effect for resin system B specimens.

Although the magnitude of the effect is much smaller, the same trends can be discerned in the properties of resin system A specimens (Fig.6), except that here the initial increase in values is proportionately smaller and the second increase occurs between 16 and 32 weeks' exposure, with very similar values being recorded after 32 and 64 weeks' exposure. As might be expected, significance tests give less positive confirmation of the effects than for system B specimens. Particularly for the tensile properties it is not difficult to imagine a set of horizontal straight lines drawn (Fig.6) to represent the sets of points. With flexural properties, however, to date there are definite upwards trends in both strength and strain results for system A specimens.

Apart from the resins used, specimens of the two systems differ only in that system A specimens were first exposed 4 weeks later than system B specimens.

In this difference lies a key to the observed behaviour. Reference to Table 4 reveals that, during equivalent periods of exposure, the weather to which specimens of the two series are subjected may differ considerably and, in particular:

(a) during the first four weeks of exposure, system A specimens received only half the radiation experienced by system B specimens;

(b) between 16 and 32 weeks' exposure, system A specimens averaged 50% more radiation than did system B specimens.

The correlation between the curves in Figs 6 and 7 and the radiation figures in Table 4 suggests that the sun's radiation initiates a cross-linking reaction which offsets the recognised deleterious effects of the weather to an extent proportional to the rate of irradiation. The exact relationship is no doubt complex and will depend on other factors such as the instantaneous rate of irradiation and the presence of free styrene monomer (which, in the absence of a high temperature post-cure, is undoubtedly still present in the specimens in significant quantities when first exposed) but, as an approximate guideline, over the period so far studied, if the time-averaged rate of irradiation exceeds a critical value in the region of 12.00–15.00 mWh/mm² per week, an increase in the magnitude of stresses and extensions at failure is observed.

The lower magnitude overall of the variations observed with system A specimens probably reflects the superior weathering properties of that resin system and also demonstrates the effectiveness of this type of laminate construction, in which a gelcoat with good weathering characteristics protects a lay-up resin incorporating other properties, in this case a degree of flame retardancy, which might lower the resin's resistance to the weather.

In addition to differences between the two resin systems, close examination reveals that the variations are more manifest in flexure than in tension, in strains and extensions than

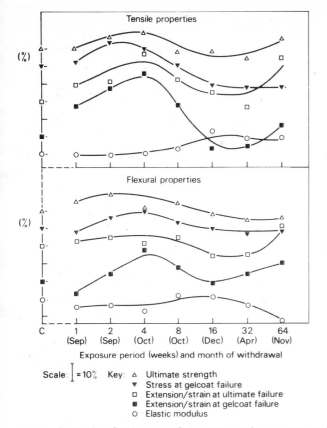

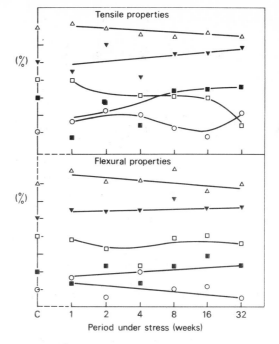

Fig.7 Properties of resin system B exposure specimens, expressed as a percentage of the equivalent value of an adjacent control specimen. The vertical scale is indicated, the first point C (= control) on each line defining 100%

Fig.8 Properties of resin system A laboratory specimens, expressed as a percentage of the equivalent value of an adjacent control specimen. The vertical scale is indicated, the first point C (= control) on each line defining 100%

in stress values, and at gelcoat failure than at ultimate failure and this is borne out by significance tests. As the gelcoat has a large external surface area which is directly exposed to the sun and through which must pass any radiation reaching the lay-up resin, it is to be expected that gelcoat failure will be affected more than ultimate failure. Also deterioration of the gelcoat, which is put in the greatest stress during flexural tests, would be expected to have a greater effect on flexural than on tensile test results. The greater changes in extensions than in stresses might be due to the plasticising action of monomer or of rainwater retained in the specimens after conditioning although there is no other evidence for this. It is more likely that it may simply reflect that the extensometer is in contact with the gelcoat while stress is principally a function of the reinforced layer, this observation thus also showing the greater susceptibility of the gelcoat.

To date flexural failure in short term testing has always occurred in the tensile face of the specimen, even though flexural specimens were tested with the upwards exposed face in compression. It seems unlikely that changes have occurred through a sufficient thickness of laminate to

affect the strength of tensile layers in flexure, and such variation as is observed is probably due to changes in the compressive layers altering the position of the neutral axis and thus the number of effective tensile layers. However, as flexural failure is a gradual process in which successive layers of mat sequentially 'peel', there is in consequence a greater scatter in flexural properties which is seen in Table 3 and in the control specimen results.

The effect of applied stress on performance is surprisingly small. Deviation from the initial values of the uts of system A specimens (Fig.6) exposed under a 25% stress, has at no time been found to exceed 5 percent and has no statistical significance. A comparison of equivalent specimens exposed under different stresses (Fig.5) suggests that stressing may actually improve a specimen's performance. However, it seems unlikely that any beneficial reaction will continue indefinitely, particularly if it is a cross-linking reaction in which free monomer plays a significant role, and the testing of laboratory stressed specimens (Fig.8 – very similar results were obtained with system B specimens) indicates that, over a 32-week period, a 25% stress without the effects of weathering reduces most of the strength properties by

Table 4. Summary of weather during 64 weeks' exposure

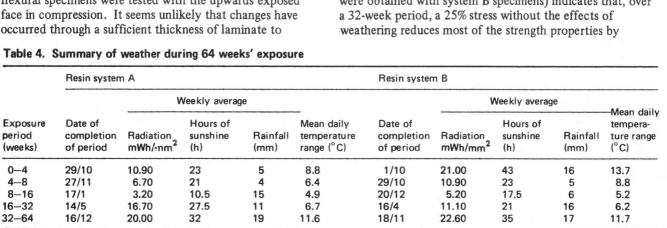

| | | Resin system A | | | | | Resin system B | | | |
| | | | Weekly average | | | | | Weekly average | | Mean daily tempera- ture range (°C) |
Exposure period (weeks)	Date of completion of period	Radiation mWh/nm²	Hours of sunshine (h)	Rainfall (mm)	Mean daily temperature range (°C)	Date of completion of period	Radiation mWh/mm²	Hours of sunshine (h)	Rainfall (mm)	
0–4	29/10	10.90	23	5	8.8	1/10	21.00	43	16	13.7
4–8	27/11	6.70	21	4	6.4	29/10	10.90	23	5	8.8
8–16	17/1	3.20	10.5	15	4.9	20/12	5.20	17.5	6	5.2
16–32	14/5	16.70	27.5	11	6.7	16/4	11.10	21	16	6.2
32–64	16/12	20.00	32	19	11.6	18/11	22.60	35	17	11.7

about 5 percent although this is barely significant. However it is anticipated that over longer periods of exposure, the deleterious effect of applied stress will become more apparent and a permanent reduction in all the strength properties will result.

Mention should here be made of the large (> 50%), superficially anomalous increase in the gelcoat failure properties of flexural system A specimens between 16 and 32 weeks' exposure. Examination of the results of individual specimens revealed that most of the increase was due to 3 specimens (within a batch of 10) in which no failure of the gelcoat could be detected prior to ultimate failure. There is some evidence to suggest that when this happens, ultimate failure values are also increased, but it is not possible to establish the statistical significance of this since such behaviour has previously been encountered far less frequently. However, the possibility of a change in failure mode and a consequent jump in values cannot be discounted, particularly as the comparative constancy of elastic modulus values in Figs 6 and 7 indicates that observed variations in failure stresses and strains are due to a change in failure point.

Table 5. Relationship between mat anisotropy and the components of tensile stress

X	0.9	0.788	0.75	0.7
R_A	−218.4	0	29.4	56.9
R_B	− 49.7	72.3	88.9	104.3
$(G_{A-1} + B_{A-1}) -$				
$(G_{B-1} + B_{B-1})$	187.7	91.3	137.3	180.2

CONCLUSIONS

A pattern of reproducible changes in several properties of glass reinforced plastics, exposed to the weather while under tensile stress, has been observed during the first 64 weeks' exposure. These changes have been observed in stresses and strains, at gelcoat failure and ultimate failure, in tension and in flexure. On average, they take the form of an increase of about 10% during the first 2–4 weeks of exposure, followed by a comparable decline over the next 30 weeks, and then a second, generally smaller, increase up to 64 weeks after the initial exposure date. Although, exceptionally, the extension at gelcoat failure of resin system B specimens increased by 30% during the first four weeks of exposure, it then declined by an equivalent of 40% of the original value during the next 12 weeks. The significance of many of these changes has been confirmed but it is notable that the ultimate tensile strength of resin system A never varied by more than 5 percent from the initial value throughout a period of 64 weeks' exposure. The changes can be explained as the result of two compensating actions, one the widely recognised deleterious weathering action and the other a strengthening reaction which correlates with the quantity of solar radiation experienced by the specimens and is probably a cross-linking reaction. Applied stress appears to have little effect at this stage, and the 5 percent decline caused by a 25% stress loading in the uts of laboratory specimens over a 32-week period is barely significant.

Although the results can only be regarded as of a short term nature in relation to the life expectancy of plastics used in building structures, they give an encouraging indication that the effect of stress may not need to become an excessive complication in carrying out structural design calculations for glass fibre reinforced plastics components intended to be used exposed to the weather.

FUTURE WORK

The results presented here form part of a continuing investigation which will include the testing of specimens after longer periods of exposure and of all laboratory specimens. Several possible reasons for the observed behaviour have been suggested and these will be tested further by more fundamental investigations.

ACKNOWLEDGEMENTS

The authors would like to thank many people who have helped with this work in various ways, but in particular we wish to express our appreciation to G. Brown, who designed and supervised the construction of the stressing equipment and to K. Sparks, who milled the several thousand specimen required.

REFERENCES

1 Read, T. and O'Brien, T. *Arch J* 157 (1973) pp 697, 817 and 1035
2 Makowski, Z. S. *Plasticonstruction* 1 No 2 (March 1971) p 53
3 *Modern Plastics* No 64 (August 1970)
4 Wade, D. J. 5th PI Design Committee Conf, Cranfield, Paper 19 (Jan 1973)
5 Allen, H. G. *Proc Inst Struct Eng* No 533 (1967)
6 Crowder, J. R., Hill, L. G. and Norris, J. F. Unpublished work
7 Crowder, J. R. BRS Miscellaneous Paper 2 (July 1964)
8 Rugger, G. R. *SPE Transactions* No 236 (July 1964)
9 Jain, R. K. and George, J. *Popular Plastics* No 39 (Oct 1970)
10 'Report of the Structural Design Data Sub-Committee on the Evaluation of Published and Unpublished Work on Long Term Properties of Reinforced Plastics', Technical Committee of the Reinforced Plastics Group, British Plastics Fed (Nov 1960)
11 Capron, E., Crowder, J. R. and Smith, R. G. BRE Current Paper 21/73 (August 1973)
12 Rawe, A. W. *Trans J Plast Inst* 30 (Feb 1962) p 27
13 Oswitch, S. *Reinforced Plastics* 8 (Dec 1963) p 116
14 Goldfein, S. *J Appl Pol Sci* 10 (1966) p 1737
15 Kabelka, J. *5th BPF Intern Reinforced Plast Conf,* London, Paper 17 (Nov 1966)
16 Werren, F. US Forest Products Lab, Reports 1811 (1950) and 1811A (1951)
17 Owen, M. J. and Howe, R. J. *J Phys D (Applied Phys)* 5 (1972) p 1637
18 Berndtsson, B. S. *Plastvarlden* 6 (1971) p 43
19 Bershtein, V. A. and Glikman, L. A. *Soviet Physics-Solid State* 5 (Feb 1964) p 1651
20 Cameron, J. B. Min of Tech D Mat Report No 145 (June 1967)
21 Steel, D. J. *Trans J Plast Inst* 33 (Oct 1965) p 161
22 Zilvar, V. *Kunstoffe* 59 No 12 (1969) p 948
23 Longchal, M. *Revue Generale du Caoutchouc et des Plastiques: Plastiques* 5 No 4 (1968) p 235
24 Barrett, D. G. and Steel, D. J. MEXE Tech Note 4/67, Min of Def (Army Dept) (May 1967)
25 Crowder, J. R. and Norris, J. F. BRE Current Paper, to be published
26 Wildman, D. Private discussion
27 Howe, R. J. PhD thesis, Nottingham University (1971)
28 Norris, J. F. *Reinforced Plastics* 18 No 12 (Dec 1974) p 335
29 British Standard 2782: 1970-Methods of Testing Plastics, Part 301L (Tensile Testing) and Part 304B (Flexural Testing)
30 Norris, J. F. *Composites* 7 No 3 (July 1976)
31 Everett, L. H. Private discussion
32 ASTM Standards D 638-68, D1708-66 and D 2289-69
33 Ball, P. and Raymond, J. A. 5th PI Design Committee Conf, Cranfield, Paper 2 (Jan 1973)

A study of failure modes in grp specimens undergoing destructive short-term tensile testing (CP 55/76)

J.F. Norris

In a separate study [1] of the long term behaviour of the material, 600 glass reinforced polyester (grp) specimens were tensile tested to destruction. Four different resin/glass systems were used, but otherwise the specimens were nominally identical in structure and dimensions.

All specimens were tested at a constant jaw separation rate of 0.0833 mm/s. For most specimens, the force and extension increased steadily up to the point where the specimen separated into two pieces at a position outside the jaws of the testing machine and the load could no longer be sustained. However, for a few specimens, the point of failure lay wholly within or aligned with the edge of one of the testing machine's jaws — such failures are hereafter referred to as gripbreaks (Fig.1). Other specimens (termed extensometer breaks) failed at the point of contact of one of the extensometer's knife-edged clamps (Fig.1). A third group of specimens (slipbreaks) slipped slightly but repeatedly within the jaws, each slip temporarily reducing the applied force (Fig.2), before ultimately failing. An abnormal failure could in each case be expected to be accompanied by a reduction in the ultimate tensile stress (uts) that the specimen could withstand — the jaws and extensometer clamps might cause crushing and notching respectively, and slipping is a severe form of fatigue. Analysis of the results revealed consistent differences between average values of groups of specimens failing in different ways, but only for extensometer breaks were the differences found to be significant reductions in uts. However, consideration of the nature of each mode of failure suggests that the observations are not incompatible with the expectations.

EXPERIMENTAL

Laminates were fabricated to a high standard of uniformity by a method reported elsewhere.[2] The materials used, laminate dimensions, the method of specimen preparation and details of testing are recorded in the accompanying paper.[1] The four laminate series produced can be

distinguished as follows:

Series	Resin system	Orientation of mat reinforcement
I	B	Lateral
II	B	Longitudinal
III	A	Lateral
IV	A	Longitudinal

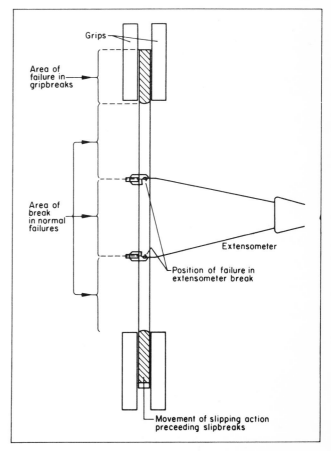

Fig.1 Positions of break defining different failure types

19

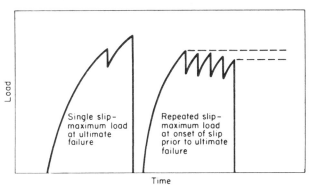

Fig.2 Typical traces of slipbreaks

RESULTS

Table 1 shows average tensile stresses at gelcoat failure (gts) and at ultimate failure (uts) of specimens of each laminate series failing in each abnormal mode and in the normal mode. Extension values (ge, ue) of the same specimen groups are presented in Table 2. Significance values are also included where they exceed 90%.

As the number of abnormal failures among specimens of Series II and IV is small, random variations would hide consistent differences of the same magnitude as those seen in the average values of Series I and III specimens. This is particularly so with Series IV specimens, where a complete reversal of the trends in average tensile stresses of Series I—III specimens is observed, but statistical tests indicate that differences among Series IV tensile strength averages are not significant.

In general, the following relationships are observed:

● For average tensile stresses at ultimate failure:

Extensometer break < normal break < slipbreak

The significance of these differences, although established for some laminate series, is not consistent. For no series was a difference of any significance found between average tensile strengths of gripbreaks and normal failures.

● For average tensile stresses at gelcoat failure, the same relationship is observed, and the gts expressed as a percentage of the uts is approximately constant within each laminate series irrespective of mode of failure. However, only one difference is significant — that of Series II extensometer breaks from normal break specimens in the same series.

● For average extensions at ultimate failure:

Gripbreak < normal break

The difference is of moderate to high significance for both major laminate series. Differences of extensometer breaks and of slipbreaks from normal breaks were in no case significant.

● Average extensions at gelcoat failure show no consistent difference whatever the failure mode.

DISCUSSION

Although differences between average tensile stresses both at gelcoat failure and at ultimate failure are not of consistent significance, it is believed that this is because, for extensometer breaks, the difference is small, as also is the number of specimens failing after slipping, and that continuing tests would eventually establish significance in all instances. The differences are consistently in the sense which would be expected for each type of break by the following arguments.

Extensometer breaks

The pressure of the extensometer knife edge slightly reduces the breaking load of the gelcoat at the point of contact, bringing it below the previous minimum for any point on the gelcoat of some specimens. Gelcoat failure for these specimens will thus occur first at the knife edge. The

Table 1. Relationship between mode of failure and average tensile strengths

| Laminate series | Average tensile stress (N/mm^2) | Normal failure | Failure type | | |
			Gripbreaks	Extensometer breaks	Slipbreaks
I	No of specimens	192	37	19	2
	gts*	56	56	55	61
	uts*	66	66	65	75 (96%)
	gts/uts (%)	85	85	84	82
II	No of specimens	38	6	4	2
	gts	49	51	44 (97%)	54
	uts	57	57	51 (96%)	62
	gts/uts (%)	87	91	87	87
III	No of specimens	195	37	11	7
	gts	53	53	51	55
	uts	69	70	68	75 (99.6%)
	gts/uts (%)	76	75	75	74
IV	No of specimens	45	3	2	0
	gts	44	41	48	—
	uts	55	51	58	—
	gts/uts (%)	81	81	83	—

*gts = tensile strength at gelcoat failure; uts = tensile strength at ultimate failure. Figures in parentheses, where given, indicate the significance of difference between strength and corresponding value of normal failure specimens. Where no figure is given, significance is less than 90%

Table 2. Relationship between mode of failure and average percentage extensions

Laminate series	Average extension (%)	Normal failure	Failure type		
			Gripbreaks	Extensometer breaks	Slipbreaks
I	No of specimens	192	37	19	2
	ge*	0.82	0.79	0.80	0.81
	ue*	1.08	1.02 (98%)	1.09	1.10
	ge/ue (%)	75	78	73	74
II	No of specimens	38	6	4	2
	ge	0.78	0.80	0.71 (97%)	0.88 (91%)
	ue	0.99	0.92	0.96	1.18
	ge/ue (%)	78	86	74	75
III	No of specimens	195	37	11	7
	ge	0.68	0.65	0.66	0.69
	ue	1.20	1.10 (99.5%)	1.21	1.22
	ge/ue (%)	57	60	54	57
IV	No of specimens	45	3	2	0
	ge	0.63	0.57	0.68	—
	ue	1.03	0.86 (91%)	1.05	—
	ge/ue (%)	61	67	65	—

*ge = extension at gelcoat failure, ue = extension at ultimate failure. Figures in parentheses, where given, indicate the significance of difference between extension and corresponding value of normal failure specimens. Where no figure is given, significance is less than 90%

knife edge will also increase the probability in all specimens of the gelcoat breaking at the point of contact prior to ultimate failure. If the knife edge can then penetrate the tip of the crack, the wedge action of the knife edge will increase the local stress in the reinforced layer at that point; thereby reducing the additional tensile stress which is required to cause ultimate failure. Thus the average tensile stresses at both gelcoat failure and ultimate failure will appear to be lower in extensometer break specimens than in specimens failing normally.

Gripbreaks

The average applied stress at which gripbreak failures occur is indistinguishable from the average tensile strength of specimens failing normally, and gripbreak failures appear to be normal failures of specimens whose weakest points lie within the testing machine's jaws. The same relationship was found [4] when scissor grips [5] were used to test a range of large grained concretes. These are complex biaxial situations, but nevertheless these observations are surprising, for the applied stress will be transferred from jaws to specimen in such a way that the force experienced by a specimen at a point within the jaws will decrease as the distance from the edge of the jaws increases. For scissor grips, it was established [4] that the strain in a specimen under stress remained constant for a short distance into the jaws, and decreased gradually thereafter. Similar conditions are expected for the rubber-faced jaws used to test the grp specimens, deformation of the rubber faces being clearly visible at high extensions. It would be expected that the breaking stress would only be approached close to the edge of the jaws, and this is confirmed by the observations that gripbreaks only occur at or near the jaw's edge, and that the proportion of specimens failing within the jaws (14%) is considerably less than the fraction of a specimen's length gripped by the jaws (39%). It would be expected that for gripbreaks occurring at some distance into the jaws, the frictional restraining force of the jaws would increase the

applied force required to cause failure, but an apparently higher average tensile strength of gripbreak specimens is not found.

The gauge length over which extension is measured forms only a portion of the specimen. For many specimens failing in the normal mode, ultimate failure occurs within the gauge length; for gripbreak specimens this is never so, and the average number of gelcoat failures within the gauge length is also expected to be less. The lower measured extensions at failure of gripbreak specimens reflect the fact that the point of ultimate failure lies outside the gauge length and suggest that the greatest extension usually occurs at the points at which the gelcoat has already failed or at which ultimate failure subsequently occurs.

Slipbreaks

Partial slipping in the testing machine jaws is a violent action in which the applied force is suddenly released and then abruptly taken up again. Such an action is obviously severely detrimental to the specimen and yet the average uts of specimens experiencing varying degrees of slipping is greater than that of specimens failing normally. This is because, for a specimen to slip, the applied force must exceed a limit set by the frictional forces holding the specimen in the jaws. Although this limit will vary with the specimen and area of contact in the jaws, it is always greater than the uts of a large proportion of specimens, and therefore only specimens of above average strength reach the friction limit before failure. It is apparent from Fig.2 that the average uts of slipbreak specimens, although greater than the average uts of normal failure specimens, is certainly lower than it would have been if slipping had not occurred. The results indicate that specimens of above average uts also reach a higher stress on average before gelcoat failure occurs.

British Standard specimen

The specimen type chosen for tensile testing in this study

differs from the corresponding British Standard specimen type in width and in the method of gripping the specimen. The narrower width of 12.7 mm corresponds to that of the British Standard flexural specimen,[6] and was adopted so that tensile and flexural test specimens could be cut from a single specimen strip which had undergone some form of pretreatment, in this case exposure under stress. No difficulties have been encountered due to the use of the narrower specimen; the narrower width does not appear to make it more susceptible to minor edge defects such as chips in the gelcoat and lay-up resins, providing the general standard of specimen preparation is high.

The British Standard [3] recommends that tensile testing is carried out, using serrated jaws, on specimens to which are bonded endpieces which reduce crushing and enhance gripping of the specimen. However, in a preliminary trial using serrated jaws, the proportion of specimens fitted with endpieces in which failure occurred at the edge of an endpiece ($\sim$ 40%) exceeded the proportion of gripbreaks ($\sim$ 30%) among specimens without endpieces; this proportion could be reduced further by using rubber-faced grips. Although the figures suggest that, like gripbreaks, the mean breaking strength of specimens failing at the edge of an endpiece is the same as the mean of specimens of the same group failing normally, there seems little point in incurring the additional work if no advantage is gained and more abnormal failures occur.

It should be borne in mind that only specimens with chopped strand mat reinforcement have been used in this study, and that the same conclusions may not apply to composites with unidirectional or woven reinforcement and consequently higher tensile strengths. However, as the method of tensile testing used in this study appears to be superior to the present British Standard method,[3] the differences should be considered for adoption within the Standard for chopped strand mat reinforced composites,

and further work should be done to investigate the suitability of the modified method for composites with other types of reinforcement. The instruction to disregard specimens breaking within the area of their endpieces and hence presumably gripbreaks also, should be reconsidered.

CONCLUSIONS

At gelcoat failure and at ultimate failure, the average tensile stresses of specimens ultimately failing in different modes increase in the order:

Extensometer break $<$ normal break $\simeq$ gripbreak $<$ slipbreak

At ultimate failure, the average extension of gripbreak specimens is significantly less than the average extensions of specimens failing in other ways. Reconsideration of the British Standard method of test is proposed.

ACKNOWLEDGEMENT

The work described has been carried out as part of the research programme of the Building Research Establishment of the Department of the Environment and this paper is published by permission of the Director.

REFERENCES

1   Norris, J. F. and Crowder, J. R. 'The weathering of glass reinforced polyesters under stress — short term behaviour', *Composites* 7 No 3 (July 1976)
2   Norris, J. F. *Reinforced Plastics* 18 No 12 (December 1974) p335
3   British Standard 2782:1970. Methods of testing plastics, Part 301L
4   Williams, R. I. T. and Kolias, S. Discussed in Dr Kolias' PhD Thesis, University of Surrey, 1975
5   Johnson, C. D. and Sidwell, E H. *Mag Concrete Res* 20 No 65 (December 1968)
6   British Standard 2782:1970. Methods of testing plastics, Part 304B

Cement-based composites

Cement-based composites with mixtures of different types of fibres (CP 80/75)

P.L. Walton and A.J. Majumdar

The interest in fibre reinforced cement and concrete is now considerable as is evidenced by the rapidly growing literature on this subject.[1,2] Hydraulic cements used in the construction industry are weak in tension and against impact so reinforcement by suitable fibres is an obvious method of overcoming these difficulties. In the past decade extensive research has been carried out on the properties of cementitious composites incorporating various types of fibre — glass, carbon, steel wire and polymer fibres being the principal ones — and, of course, the use of asbestos for strengthening cement has been known to the industry for a very long time.

Several years ago Goldfein[3] demonstrated that the inherent brittleness of cement pastes or mortars can be remedied by incorporating into these matrices very small quantities of organic polymer fibres such as nylon or polypropylene. This work led to a more comprehensive investigation of the prospects for fibrous reinforcement of Portland cement concrete by Williamson[4] in which polymer fibres were again shown to impart a high degree of resistance against shattering. Several applications based on this property were suggested and in one novel application[5] in the UK, fibrillated polypropylene tape is now used in the manufacture of pile shells replacing the more conventional steel reinforcement.

Although polymer fibres do improve the impact strength of a cementitious matrix very effectively, because of their low modulus of elasticity accompanied by large extensibilities under stress it is doubtful whether they can make a significant contribution towards an increase in the tensile strength of the material. It is necessary, therefore, to consider the possibilities that might result from the addition of a suitable second fibre to the polymer fibre, for applications where improvements in both tensile strength and resistance against impact are desired.

Some experimental work has been carried out in this area at the Building Research Station, using various combinations of fibres and the results are presented here.

MATERIALS

Among organic polymer fibres polypropylene and nylon were selected for this study. Several different types of the two fibres were used. For polypropylene, 1000, 6000, 12000 denier* fibrillated yarn, 1000 denier tape and 170 denier (150 μm diameter) monofilaments were tried whereas for nylon 24 (54 μm diameter) and 4 (23 μm diameter) denier monofilaments were used.

As the second fibre (additional to the polymer fibre) glass, asbestos and carbon fibre were tried. A prototype alkali-resistant glass fibre,[6] Cem-Fil,** was supplied in the form of rovings consisting of 30 strands each having 204 filaments of 13 μm diameter. Asbestos used was of the chrysotile type of a grade suitable for reinforcing cement. The carbon fibre was in the form of either a chopped-strand mat, or a continuous tow. In fact all the different types of fibre were supplied by their respective manufacturers and were used in the 'as received' condition; several batches of ordinary Portland cement (OPC), each passing the British Standard BS 12, were also used.

FABRICATION

All composites were produced in the form of flat sheets about 9 mm thick and cut into test specimens 50 mm wide and 152 mm long. Two principal methods have been used to produce the composites; these were the pre-mixing method and the spray-suction method.[7] In both methods

---

* Denier is a measure of the 'diameter' or size of the yard and is numerically equal to the weight in grammes of 9 km of the yarn.

** Registered trade mark of Pilkington Brothers Ltd

the cement slurry was de-watered by suction from the underside of the mould.

In the pre-mixing method a fairly wet slurry of cement and water was prepared in the ratio of 1:0.5 and the chopped fibres added and mixed in by hand. Sometimes an additive such as polyethylene oxide was used to assist the mixing of the fibres. The mix was poured into the mould having dimensions of either 280 x 330 mm or 450 x 450 mm, trowelled flat and de-watered. The smaller moulds were placed in a press and lightly pressed to assist de-watering and compaction.

In the spray-suction method the slurry, which sometimes contained premixed short fibres, was sprayed through a nozzle and atomised with an air jet. Fibres were introduced into the slurry spray in an air stream while the spray head traversed a mould 4 m long and 1 m wide to cover it uniformly with the mixture of slurry and fibres. To provide a mixture of glass and polypropylene fibres two separate choppers were used and these delivered the requisite amounts of the two fibres onto the mould. The mixture did not require spreading over the mould and the composite sheet was de-watered and trowelled flat.

Two boards containing glass crenette and carbon fibre random mat respectively were layed up by hand in a sandwich form with the fibre layers near the top and bottom surfaces and the central region reinforced with organic fibres. The fibre contents of all boards were expressed as percentages by weight, based on the weights of the boards after they had been de-watered.

CURING CONDITIONS

All boards were cured for 7 days under a covering of damp sacking before being cut into sample coupons. The coupons were then stored in some or all of a number of conditions designed to subject the material to conditions likely to be met in service and one condition designed to accelerate the effect of ageing on the material. In one set of experiments the samples were stored in air in a room whose temperature was controlled at 18°C and humidity at 40% RH. For water storage the samples were kept completely submerged in water at 18°C. For the natural weathering condition, samples were placed on a wire mesh off the ground and in a horizontal position on an exposure site at Garston. Samples were also put into glass jars filled with water and sealed. The temperature of the water was maintained at 60°C. Storage time for air (A), water (W), and natural weathering (NW) was estimated from the day of casting, whereas for accelerated curing it was reckoned from the time the temperature of the samples reached 60°C.

TEST METHODS

Tests were carried out on the composite materials to determine their flexural and tensile strength and their impact resistance. The flexural strength was determined by subjecting the 152 x 50 x 9 mm test specimens to uniform bending in a four point loading rig. The maximum stress (modulus of rupture) was calculated assuming elastic behaviour. The impact resistance was determined using the Izod Pendulum method, the maximum energy of the pendulum being 12.5 J. The specimens were clamped so that they were subjected to bending in the same plane as in the bending test. Specimens which did not fail under the first blow were given another and the energy of the two added. The energy absorbed was divided by the cross sectional area of the specimen. The tensile strength was determined in the usual way with the 152 x 50 x 9 mm specimen clamped at each end and loaded axially.

It was thought desirable to obtain some idea of the strength of the bond between the polymer fibre and the cementitious matrix. A simple pull-out technique used in this laboratory previously [8] was chosen. Ritchie and Mackintosh [9] have recently reported on pull-out forces required to extract fibrillated polypropylene from concrete. In the present study, polypropylene monofilaments of 150 μm diameter were embedded in a matrix of cement paste in such a way that the fibre protruded from both faces of the disc to which it was perpendicularly disposed. After curing under specified conditions, the specimen was loaded in a tensile testing machine, with the lower end of the fibre clamped directly in jaws attached to the crosshead of the machine.

Fibre embedment lengths of 10 mm and 20 mm were selected and pull-out specimens were prepared using water-to-cement ratios of 0.3, 0.35 and 0.4. Curing conditions were the same as described above and the samples were tested after 7 days, 28 days and 180 days of storage under different environments.

RESULTS

The strength of unreinforced cement paste depends strongly on the water to cement ratio, the degree of compaction achieved and the presence of cracks due to voids or drying shrinkage. The values for the modulus of rupture obtained with boards used as control, in which fibres were absent, were found to vary widely but were normally around 7 to 10 MN/m². The values for the impact strength of plain cement ranged from 1.4 to 2 kJ/m².

Most of the experimental work in this study has been carried out with polypropylene fibres either singly or in mixtures incorporating other fibres, notably glass. The strength results of cement composites having various amounts of polypropylene fibre are given in Table 1 for the different curing conditions used. In Table 2, strength data obtained when mixtures of polypropylene and glass fibres were used in various proportions are given. For each board listed, the method of fabrication is also given in these tables. In Table 3, the tensile strength results of some of the composites are presented.

The values obtained for the impact strength and the modulus of rupture of these composites kept under water at 60°C have been plotted against the age of test specimens in Figs. 1 and 2.

The modulus of rupture and impact strength values of cement composites reinforced by nylon fibres are given in Table 4. Similar experimental data obtained from boards having asbestos, glass and carbon fibres respectively as reinforcement are given in Table 5. Table 6 gives the strength results of composite samples incorporating various mixtures of fibres. Again, the method of fabrication used in individual cases is also listed in these tables.

In the work described above, at least 6 samples were tested at each experimental point. In general, the coefficients of variation were 12% for modulus of rupture and tensile strength and 20% for impact strength measurements.

The load/extension curves recorded during the pull-out tests are schematically shown in Fig.3. Two different types of

Table 1. Properties of composites reinforced with polypropylene fibres

| No | type | denier | length | wt | Fabrication method | Curing | Modulus of rupture (MN/m²) | | | | | Impact strength (kJ/m²) | | | | |
							7d*	28d	60d	180d	1 yr	7d	28d	60d	180d	1 yr
B'	fib	1000	20mm	1.0%	pre-mix and press	water	7.8					8.6				
						60°C			10.5					6.8		
G'	fib	1000	51mm	1.0%	pre-mix	water	11.1					8.1				
						60°C		8.4	8.6					7.2	7.2	
Wd1	fib	1000	20mm	1.0%	spray-up	water	6.6		7.0	4.9	6.8	6.5		5.8	5.6	6.3
						NW				6.1	6.7				6.0	6.3
						60°C			8.7	6.9	5.6			6.1	6.3	6.1
A'	tape	1000	20mm	1.0%	pre-mix and press	water	8.2					9.3				
						60°C			10.0					8.2		
C'	tape	1000	51mm	1.0%	pre-mix and press	water	6.7					13.8				
						60°C			7.9					8.8		
I'	fib	12000	20mm	2.0%	pre-mix	water	7.4					9.1				
						60°C			7.6	7.6					4.9	8.4
Wd2	mono	170	20mm	0.8%	spray-up	water	10.2	11.1		6.1	5.3	12.8	12.8		11.0	10.9
						NW				9.0					10.9	
						60°C		12.5		5.6	5.6			12.1	11.2	11.4
Y12	mono	170	25mm	1.0%	spray-up	air		8.7		7.3			11.7			14.4
						water	7.4	9.0		10.3		11.7	11.0			12.8
						NW				5.7						12.6
						60°		8.1					11.7			
Ym2	mono	170	51mm	1.0%	spray-up	air		8.0	9.1	6.9			19.3		18.2	17.5
						water	5.9	9.5	8.0	9.0		18.6	20.7		21.5	17.9
						NW			8.8	5.3					15.4	17.5
						60°C		6.0					18.0			
Yn2	mono	170	51mm	1.1%	spray-up	air		11.2	12.7	12.0			23.5		25.7	20.8
						water	12.9	10.1	13.7	12.4		23.6	21.4		21.4	22.8
						NW			12.6	14.9					19.3	20.0
						60°C		12.7		12.9			18.2			17.3
Xy	mono	170	51mm	2.3%	spray-up	air			17.9							26.4
						water	11.0	10.1	14.5			25.7	26.4			21.2
						NW			15.2							21.7
						60°C		8.7					24.2			
Yg2 **	mono	170	51mm	2.3%	spray-up	air		12.6	14.0				26.1		27.5	
						water	11.6	13.2	15.2		15.9	29.2	27.1		25.4	24.7
						NW			15.3							21.2
						60°C		15.8	15.6				27.8		24.5	
Ye	mono	170	51mm	2.8%	spray-up	air		16.9	16.3	17.4			38.0		43.6	33.4
						water	14.6	15.7	15.7	19.1		59.2	41.7		35.2	33.4
						NW				19.6						33.6
						w60°C		18.7	19.7				38.7		38.4	

*d = days, ** = matrix contains 33% sand

curves were obtained. One type (a and b) is similar to the trace given by polypropylene fibre alone in tension. The other (c and d) displays a distinct yield point at a low load. The trace beyond this point has a reduced slope which extends up to a maximum load at which the fibre either fractures or pulls out of the matrix (at a reduced load). The yield point usually corresponds to the load at which the free end of the fibre begins to be pulled through the matrix. The numbers of traces where a yield point was detectable amounted to 58% of the total in the case of the 10 mm fibre embedment length and 53% when the depth of embedment was 20 mm.

During the pull-out experiments, a large number of fibres broke instead of being extracted from the matrix. This could be due either to wide variation in fibre strengths or to stronger interfacial adhesion or both. In these cases, the true bond strength cannot be determined, only a lower bound may be set by dividing the load by the nominal surface area of the bond.

Values of maximum load including those cases where the fibre broke and of yield load are shown in graphical form in Fig.4. Ten samples were tested in all experiments and each point on the graph represents an average of the results of these. The differences in the values ascribable to changes in the curing conditions or water-to-cement ratios were found not to be statistically significant, except in the case of samples which were prepared with a fibre embedment length of 10 mm and using a water-to-cement ratio of 0.4. These gave significantly lower values – 601 g for the maximum load and 236 g for the yield load. The corresponding mean values for all other samples with a 10 mm depth of embedment were 680 g and 295 g respectively. The mean values for 20 mm fibre embedment lengths were 687 g and 329 g. Bond strength results computed from these

Table 2. Properties of composites reinforced with mixtures of polypropylene and glass

No	Polypropylene type	length	wt	Glass wt	Fabrication method	Curing	Modulus of rupture (MN/m²) 7d	28d	180d	1 yr	Impact strength (kJ/m²) 7d	28d	180d	1 yr
Wa1	1000d fibr	20mm	1.0%	5.0%	spray-up	W	27.3	29.6	27.1	24.6	18.8	14.6	13.1	14.0
						NW			34.7	29.2			19.1	15.7
						60°C		16.8		12.0		8.2		6.2
Wb	6000d fibr	20mm	1.0%	5.0%	spray-up	W	27.8	25.1	23.2	20.2	19.9	16.6	16.3	13.4
						NW			29.8	25.9			21.2	22.4
						60°C		16.5		13.1		8.1		3.9
Wc	170d mono	20mm	1.0%	5.0%	spray-up	W	27.4	33.0	29.3	24.5	24.9	23.5	19.6	18.2
						NW			34.8	31.7			28.7	22.6
						60°C		15.8	15.4	14.3		9.8	11.9	10.8
Vk	1000d tape	20mm	1.0%	5.0%	spray-up	A			25.5	24.6			25.5	23.6
						W	24.1	25.6	22.2	21.0	22.6	24.5	17.5	11.1
						NW			29.3	24.0			23.0	19.8
						60°C		14.8	10.5	9.7		8.7	7.1	6.7
N′	1000d fibr	51mm	0.9%	1.2% crenette	hand lay-up	W	28.1				28.7			
						60°C		14.2*				10.5*		
D′	1000d fibr	51mm	0.5%	2.0%	pre-mix and press	W	14.1				12.9			
						60°C		12.4*				7.0*		
Xu	170d mono	51mm	0.9%	5.0%	spray-up	A			33.1	35.0			35.4	32.4
						W	33.4	35.1	21.8	19.3	35.4	31.9	24.0	18.6
						NW			35.0	27.3			29.6	25.9
						60°C		16.5	7.9	7.3		20.8	13.5	16.3
Yb	170d mono	51mm	2.3%	4.0%	spray-up	A		28.3	28.8	27.8		45.9	44.5	50.4
						W	23.8	24.3	21.6	18.3	58.7	51.1	37.8	33.4
						NW		25.6	29.7	24.6		50.8	37.3	36.8
						60°C		14.2	14.0	16.0		32.2	33.1	25.0
Yc	170d mono	51mm	1.2%	4.3%	spray-up	A		38.7	33.7	31.4		33.1	31.2	29.2
						W	33.6	36.5	22.7	20.7	33.1	32.6	20.0	20.0
						NW		31.6	31.6	27.6		32.9	28.4	23.1
						60°C		16.3	9.2	9.1		17.0	15.4	13.1
Yd**	170d mono	51mm	1.1%	4.3%	spray-up	A		30.4	28.0	25.6		35.0	32.7	31.2
						W	22.6	22.4	24.1	24.1	29.6	29.8	26.6	25.9
						NW		23.3	25.8	24.5		35.6	30.3	28.2
						60°C		17.3	11.2	11.0		17.5	19.8	18.2
Yf	1000d fibr	51mm	1.0%	4.3%	spray-up	A		33.6	31.8	33.0		28.0	26.6	25.2
						W	36.0	33.0	21.5	19.4	26.8	25.4	14.7	11.9
						NW			28.5	24.2			19.4	15.4
						60°C		15.4	8.0	7.8		10.9	7.5	6.7
Yg1***	170d mono	51mm	1.0%	4.5%	spray-up	A		27.7	26.2	25.4		28.5	28.4	27.5
						W	23.7	25.5	17.9	18.1	28.9	28.5	19.6	17.2
						NW				21.7				18.6
						60°C		15.2	13.9	11.8		14.4	12.4	15.8
Y11	170d mono	25mm	1.0%	4.0%	spray-up	A		33.8	29.9	30.3		29.6	26.8	28.4
						W	33.8	31.7	24.4	20.0	31.2	26.6	18.4	18.0
						NW			26.9	25.7			20.5	21.9
						60°C		14.0		12.7		14.2		14.4
Ym1	170d mono	51mm	0.6%	4.1%	spray-up	A		30.9	28.0	29.0		25.6	28.4	28.4
						W	32.1	28.6	22.0	19.7	29.4	23.8	16.6	16.3
						NW			24.1	23.2			18.7	19.8
						60°C		13.7	12.5	13.5		12.1	10.3	10.9
Yn1	170d mono	51mm	1.7%	3.0%	spray-up	A		22.9	21.7	23.4		29.6	30.6	30.6
						W	23.9	31.4	15.0	16.0	34.5	32.6	25.4	21.4
						NW			19.5	18.3			23.3	26.8
						60°C		13.4	14.2	12.5		22.8	23.5	22.9

* curing time 60 days, ** matrix contains 40% pfa, *** matrix contains 33% sand

Table 3. Tensile strength of various composites

No	Type	Form	Length	wt	Glass wt	Curing	Tensile strength (MN/m²)			
							7d	28d	180d	1 yr
Vk	poly-propylene	tape 1000d	19 mm	1.0%	5.0%	air				10.3
						water	11.7	10.7		8.8
						NW				9.2
						60°C		5.7		2.1
Yf	poly-propylene	fib 1000d	51 mm	1.0%	4.3%	air		13.2	11.1	11.1
						water		12.7	7.1	8.8
						NW			9.6	9.9
						60°C		7.5	2.3	3.1
Yc	poly-propylene	mono 170d	51 mm	1.2%	4.3%	air		13.4	12.4	11.7
						water		11.9	9.3	8.8
						NW			9.9	8.8
						60°C		5.2	3.3	2.9
Yd*	poly-propylene	mono 170d	51 mm	1.1%	4.3%	air		11.1	10.2	9.9
						water		9.0	8.5	9.7
						NW		9.4	8.6	9.0
						60°C		5.5	3.4	3.4
Yb	poly-propylene	mono 170d	51 mm	2.3%	4.0%	air		10.3	9.2	10.2
						water		9.1	7.6	7.3
						NW		8.9	9.2	8.4
						60°C		5.6	4.4	6.0
Xy	poly-propylene	mono	51 mm	2.3%	—	water	4.4			
Ye	poly-propylene	mono 170d	51 mm	2.8%	—	air		5.7		
						water		5.6		
						NW				
						60°C		5.9		
Yg 1**	poly-propylene	mono 170d	51 mm	1.0%	5.0%	air		9.9	8.8	9.2
						water		9.3	6.4	7.0
						NW				7.8
						60°C		3.8	2.9	2.8
Yg 2*	poly-propylene	mono 170d	51 mm	2.3%	—	air		4.7		
						water		6.7		
						NW				
						60°C		4.4		
Yz	nylon	mono 50d	51 mm	0.2%	4.0%	air		11.7		
						water		10.3		
						60°C		3.9		
We	carbon		11 mm	1.3%	—	water	11.4			10.8
						NW				10.3

* Matrix contains 40% pfa (pulverised fly ash), ** Matrix contains 33% sand

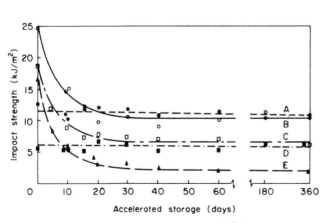

Fig.1   Impact strength versus storage time at 60°C

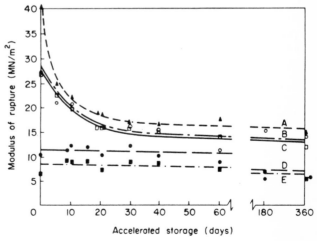

Fig.2   Modulus of rupture versus storage time at 60°C

Table 4. Properties of composites reinforced with nylon fibres

No	denier	monofilament length	wt	Fabrication method	Curing	MOR* (MN/m²) 7d	60d	IS** (kJ/m²) 7d	60d
Va	24	25 mm	0.5%	pre-mix and spray	water 60°C	7.1		7.4	
H'	24	25 mm	2.0%	pre-mix and spray	water 60°C	11.2	9.1	21.8	18.9
J'	24	25 mm	4.0%	pre-mix	water 60°C	9.0	10.5	29.3	29.8
K'	24	25 mm	3.3%	pre-mix	water 60°C	9.1	9.5	23.9	27.7
F'	4	13 mm	1.0%	pre-mix	water 60°C	11.2	9.7	7.9	5.2
Zi	50	51 mm	0.9%	spray-up	air		6.9***		8.4***
					water	7.5	10.5***	13.5	9.6***
					60°C		8.2***		10.9***

* Modulus of rupture, ** Impact strength, *** Curing 28 days

Table 5. Properties of composites reinforced with carbon, glass and asbestos fibres

No	Material	Length	wt	Fabrication method	Curing	MOR* (MN/m²) 7d	60d	1 yr	IS** (kJ/m²) 7d	60d	1 yr
CARI	carbon	32 mm	0.6%	spray-up	water 60°C	21.6			3.6		
CAR2	carbon	32 mm	0.9%	spray-up	water 60°C	24.4			2.5		
WE	carbon	11 mm	1.3%	spray-up	air		29.2				3.0
					water	31.9	28.4		3.4		3.9
					NW		33.2				3.7
					60°C		27.6***	28.8		4.0***	3.6
E'	glass	32 mm	2.0%	pre-mix and press	water	10.5			6.4		
					60°C		14.1			2.2	
Wa2	glass	32 mm	5.0%	spray-up	water	41.5		26.2	16.7		9.4
					NW		34.0				14.2
					60°C		17.6	14.8		1.9	1.8
A	asbestos	—	10%	pre-mix and spray	water	12.3		16.3	2.1		2.0
					60°C		13.8	13.0		1.8	2.2

* Modulus of rupture, ** Impact strength, *** Curing 28 days

Table 6. Properties of composites reinforced with mixtures of fibres

No	Denier	Length	wt	Second fibre type	wt	Fabrication method	Curing	MOR (MN/m²) 7d	28d	180d	1 yr	IS (kJ/m²) 7d	28d	180d	1 yr
A+N	4	12 mm	1.0%	asbestos	10%	pre-mix and spray	water	12.8	14.4	16.2	16.5	6.1	5.7	6.4	5.4
							60°C		14.6	14.8	15.2		4.1	6.2	5.7
Uz	4	12 mm	0.5%	glass	4.0%	pre-mix and spray	air			15.7	12.6			6.0	5.7
							water	26.1		17.1	14.5	13.3		5.6	6.1
							NW			14.3	13.6			5.6	5.7
							60°C		14.2				5.7		
Yz	50	51 mm	0.2%	glass	4.0%	spray-up	air		31.5				19.2		
							water	30.1	28.7			20.0	15.1		
							60°C		11.8				3.3		
ZiA	50	51 mm	0.9%	glass	4.5%	spray-up	air		37.9				29.4		
							water	35.9	36.5			30.8	24.9		
							60°C		14.8				11.2		
O'	polypropylene 1000	50 mm	1%	carbon mat	0.7%	hand lay-up sandwich form	water 60°C	15.1		17.0*		10.4		8.5*	

* 60 days curing

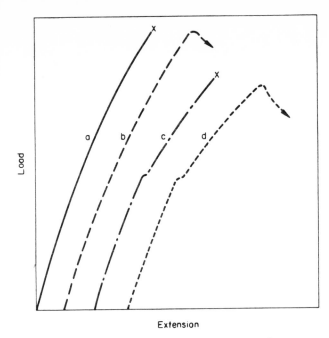

Fig.3 Schematic representation of polypropylene pull-out traces

Table 7. Results of polypropylene pull-out tests

Sample type	Breaks %	Yields %	Yield stress N/mm²	Maximum stress N/mm²
20 mm	68	53	0.337	0.704
10 mm	60	58	0.604	1.392
10 mm; 0.4 W/C ratio	50	84	0.483	1.230

because of their larger surface area which is available for bonding to the matrix.

The high modulus high strength fibres, namely carbon and asbestos, have both been used to produce composites with increased modulus of rupture, but they show very little improvement in impact strength over that of the plain matrix. The composites do not, however, deteriorate with ageing even in accelerated storage conditions. Glass fibres produce composites with greatly improved modulus of rupture and impact strength but the maintenance of these properties over long periods is still the subject of investigation and some loss of strength with time is known to occur, its extent depending on storage conditions.

When used as mixtures, the organic and the inorganic fibres work together, to produce improvement in both tensile and impact properties. The reinforcement of the matrix increases linearly with fibre content until a limiting value is reached. The limit is determined by the amount of fibre which can be added with uniform dispersion and without increasing the porosity of the matrix. This amount will vary with the length, diameter and type of fibre and with the method of fabrication. Using the pre-mixing method,

figures are given in the last two columns of Table 7; the coefficient of variation was in the range 20–30%.

DISCUSSION

The organic fibres used have very little effect on the modulus of rupture of the matrix but can impart high impact resistance which is not diminished by ageing. The longer and finer fibres have given the best results so far, presumably

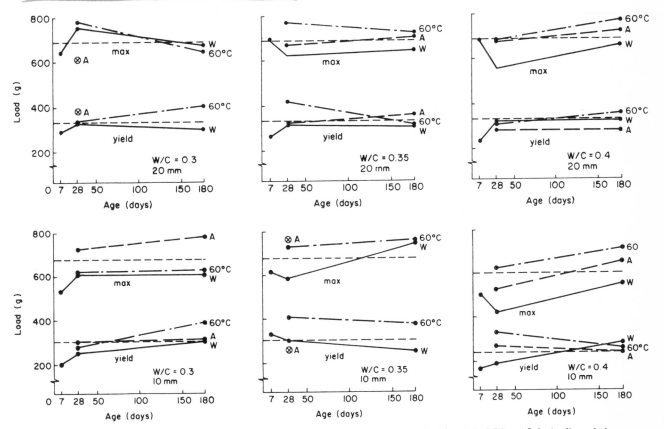

Fig.4 Graphs of maximum load and yield load vs storage time for water: cement ratios (W/C) of 0.3, 0.35 and 0.4; the figure below the W/C ratios gives the fibre embedment

the optimum amount for the organic fibres used in this series is in the range 1–2 per cent. The spray-up method can be used successfully with quantities well over 5 per cent.

The high impact resistance of the composite containing the organic fibres is derived from the stretching and pull-out of the fibres which occur at large strains after the failure of the matrix and at a lower load. It would be advantageous if the composites could be designed to support an increasing load after the cracking of the matrix. This may be achieved by improving the stress transfer from the matrix to the fibres after matrix failure: the stress transfer between matrix and fibre will depend on the aspect ratio of the fibres and the interfacial shear strength. There are possibilities for improving both these parameters by the use of finer, longer fibres; alteration of the surface characteristics; and modification of the matrix.

The pull-out experiments aimed at measuring the strength of the interfacial bond between polypropylene fibre and cement paste gave widely variable results, confirming the observations of previous studies.[8,9] One particular feature of these experiments was that in a large number of cases the fibres broke rather than pulled out of the matrix. This indicates either poor fibre strength or superior bond strength in some cases, or both. The computed maximum bond strength using all results (Table 7) is only of the order of 1 MN/m^2. This low value almost certainly means that the bond is entirely frictional in character. It is, however, little affected by changes in the environment in which the composite is placed.

CONCLUSIONS

Cement-based composites can be produced using a mixture of organic and inorganic fibres which exhibit the advantages of both. The accelerated testing results indicate that the high impact strength derived from the organic fibres, such as nylon and polypropylene, will remain stable over very long periods of time in normal use. Improved behaviour in bending may be obtainable with organic fibres by improving the stress transfer to the fibres and by using higher volume fractions.

The strength of the bond between polymer fibres and cement or concrete is likely to be poor. A value of the order of 1 MN/m^2 has been obtained with polypropylene monofilament. This poor interfacial bond is largely responsible for the excellent impact strength of polypropylene fibre cement composites. However, for these composites to be of practical value their tensile and bending properties must be improved. This can easily be accomplished by adding a second fibre such as glass or asbestos to these composites.

ACKNOWLEDGEMENTS

The work described has been carried out as part of the research programme of the Building Research Establishment of the Department of the Environment and this paper is published by permission of the Director. The collaboration with Pilkington Brothers Ltd is acknowledged.

REFERENCES

1 'Fibre-reinforced cement composites', *Report 51.067* (Materials Technology Division of the Concrete Society, London, July 1973)

2 'State-of-the-art report on fibre reinforced concrete', *Title No 70–65 American Concrete Institute Journal* (prepared by ACI Committee 544, November 1973)

3 Goldfein, S. 'Fibrous reinforcement for Portland cement', *Modern Plastics* 42 No 8 (1965) pp 156–160

4 Williamson, G. R. 'Fibrous reinforcement for Portland cement concrete', *US Clearing House AD 465999* (1965)

5 Fairweather, A. D. 'The use of polypropylene film fibre to increase impact resistance of concrete', *Proceedings International Building Exhibition Conference on 'Prospects for fibre reinforced construction materials', London 1971* (Building Research Station, Watford 1972) pp 41–43

6 Majumdar, A. J. and Ryder, J. F. 'Glass fibre reinforcement of cement products', *Glass Technology* 9 No 3 (1968) pp 78–84 and *UK patent 1243973*

7 Steele, B. R. 'Glass fibre reinforced cement', *Proceedings International Building Exhibition conference on 'Prospects for fibre reinforced construction materials' London 1971* (Building Research Station, Watford 1972) pp 29–39

8 de Vekey, R. C. and Majumdar, A. J. 'Determining bond strength in fibre-reinforced composites', *Magazine of Concrete Research* 20 No 65 (1968) pp 229–234

9 Ritchie, A. G. B. and Mackintosh, D. M. 'Selection and rheological characteristics of polypropylene fibres, *Concrete* 6 No 8 (1972) pp 36–39

Properties of glass fibres in cement environment (CP 24/77)

A.J. Majumdar, J.M. West and L.J. Larner

INTRODUCTION

In recent years the reinforcement of cement and concrete by glass fibres has attracted attention[1,2] and special alkali-resistant (AR-) glass compositions[3] have been developed for this purpose. Such a composition, containing a fairly large proportion of ZrO_2, is commercially available from Fibreglass Ltd under the trade mark Cem-FIL. The mechanical properties of Portland cement composites incorporating this particular fibre have already been subjected to detailed investigations[4,5]; some information on their long-term behaviour and versatility in manufacture and use is also available[6].

In order to judge whether these cement composites will have an acceptable level of strength after say, 20 years, it is necessary to have some idea of the changes that might take place in fibre properties during this time. The present study was initiated to provide such information for AR-glass of the same type as that sold by Fibreglass Ltd using fibres which had been (a) in cement extracts, and (b) in cement composites. Some work was also done on asbestos fibres removed from weathered asbestos cement products.

EXPERIMENTAL

The experimental glass fibres used in the present work were of the composition (weight per cent); SiO_2 71, ZrO_2 16, Na_2O 12, and Li_2O 1. Single uncoated filaments were produced in the laboratory and these were reacted with aqueous cement extracts. Glass fibre-reinforced cement composites were produced by a spray-suction method[6] and kept in various environments for specified periods. The commercially produced AR-fibres were then extracted from the cement composites and their strengths measured at specified intervals.

Glass fibre drawing

Continuous filaments of the Zirconosilicate glass were produced using the single-tip furnace assembly described by De Vekey and Majumdar[7]. Some new attachments were developed during the course of the present study which facilitated the production of fibres of uniform diameters in separate batch operations. The most important of these attachments is an arrangement, operated by a tachometer circuit, which displays the fibre drawing velocity on a meter reading

linearly up to 12 000 revolutions of the winding drum per minute. The circuit includes an uncovered transistor mounted beneath the winding drum shaft which is so machined that light from a source above it falls on the drum only during half of each drum revolution. To calibrate the meter a simple stroboscope is mounted on the end of the motor shaft. Knowing the circumference of the winding drum it is easy to calibrate the display dial in m sec^{-1}.

In monitoring the rate of glass flow, the size of the nipple is much more important than the head of glass in the crucible and by trial and error it was found that a nipple having an internal diameter of 2.5 to 3.0 mm was satisfactory for the production of glass filaments of approximately 10 μm diameter.

Fibres were collected on a 150 mm wide drum made from PVC and having a circumference of 356 mm. The drum was mounted on a trolley which could be driven to and fro every 15 sec by a reciprocating arm. This spread the glass fibre pulled over $\sim$80mm of the width of the drum, evenly distributing any diameter variations and enabling greater amounts of glass to be drawn in one run. This method was used to prepare fibres for the cement extract work. Without disrupting the normal drawing of the fibre, the reciprocating arm could be un-coupled thus converting to a fixed system. When un-coupled the machine could be used to produce a series of separate bands of uniform diameter by moving the drum laterally in short jerks.

To avoid the need for continuous observation of fibres for accidental breakage, an alarm system was designed. This consisted of three thermistors (mounted 200 mm below the glass melt) which could be moved close to the fibre when required. The thermistors are mounted in series with a relay, a variable resistance and an electric power source. As the fibre is pulled, warm air drawn along the fibre heats the thermistors. The circuit is so adjusted that the relay is maintained in a 'just closed' position during the fibre drawing. When the fibre breaks, the temperature of the thermistors falls and the relay opens, setting off the alarm.

The diameter of a fibre of given density is related to the weight of the fibre pulled per minute and the fibre

Table 1 Fibre drawing velocity and production rates

Weight of crucible plus glass (g)	Time(min) after full drawing velocity has been reached	Usual rate of flow of glass (g min⁻¹) based upon previous runs	Velocity (m sec⁻¹)* required to draw fibre of 9.15 μm diameter	Weight (g) of fibre in 1 min samples during a run
115.4				
113.3 approx	0	0.368	35.8	
	6			0.366
	10	0.365	35.6	
	20	0.362	35.3	
	21			0.361
	30	0.358	34.9	
	34			0.359
	40	0.354	34.5	
	50	0.350	34.1	
	54			0.347
94.3	55 Stopped			

*Calculated from the usual flow rate and a fibre density of 2.60 g cm⁻³

drawing velocity. For a fibre diameter of ∿9 μm, a table linking these parameters was drawn up from which it was possible to judge the correct fibre drawing velocity for a given output rate (Table 1). This table was based upon preliminary records of the glass flow rate through a particular crucible. An example of the rate of fibre production for a particular run is also included.

Corrosion experiments

With cement extracts

To study the effect of corrosion on glass fibre strength, uncoated continuous filaments having a nominal diameter of ∿9 μm were reacted with the aqueous extracts of typical ordinary Portland cements. These extracts were prepared by rolling polyethylene bottles containing mixtures of cement and distilled water for a period of 16 days. Two batches of cements were used (nos. 737 and 739), and reactions with the glass fibre were carried out at 20 and 65°C over extended periods of time. The details of the compositions of the cements and the preparative procedures for the extracts have been given elsewhere[8].

After digestion and removal of the bulk of the extract, the fibres were treated with 2N acetic acid, washed with water followed by a further treatment with 5N hydrochloric acid. Finally, the fibres were washed with water and dried at room temperature and stored in screw capped bottles prior to testing.

With fibres from the composite

Commercially made AR-glass fibres were extracted from cement composite boards which were made by the spray suction method and stored in different environmental conditions for investigating their long-term durability[9]. The fibres were obtained from a portion, about 50 mm x 35mm, cut from the main test pieces and split centrally in the plane of the board to expose the fibre strands. These segments were placed in cold (about 2°C) hydrochloric acid solution (conc HCl:H₂O = 1:2) for 10 minutes, rinsed in distilled water for a further 10

minutes and then dried on paper tissues for 20 minutes. The strands from the split faces, which by this time could be peeled away from the matrix, were then mounted on polyethylene frames, rinsed in acetone and dried. Several filaments (at least 15) were then removed from the strands, their diameter measured and immediately afterwards they were tested for strength on the balance rig (see Figure 2).

In addition to those extracted from the cured boards, fibres were taken from the 'green' board immediately after spraying. A specimen of the roving used in the production of the boards was also stored in the laboratory in a polyethylene bag to serve as the reference material. Fibres from this sample and others described above were tested after stipulated intervals of time.

Two weathered asbestos cement boards were selected for obtaining strength data on reacted asbestos fibres. One board had undergone 4 years of exposure on site before it was stored in the laboratory for a further period of 2 years. With the other board the corresponding periods were 7 and 2 years respectively. Experiments were also carried out with fibres from an unweathered asbestos cement board. It should be appreciated that these three boards were not produced at the same time and possibly neither by the same manufacturer.

By placing 100 mm x 50 mm pieces of asbestos cement sheets edgewise between the jaws of a press and applying pressure, it was possible to cleave the specimens in such a way that fibre bundles could be removed from the composite. This was achieved by careful manipulation with a sharp needle and a pair of tweezers with flat smooth faces under a binocular microscope. After the removal of the adhering matrix a quantity of fibre bundles, not less than 4 mm in length and having overall diameter in the range 15 to 40 μm, were selected for strength determinations.

Property measurements

Fibre diameter

The diameter of the glass fibres before and after corrosion was measured with the help of a microscope provided with a Watson image shearing eyepiece. A 10 μm graticule was used for calibration. For routine measurements, two 4 mm wide strips of double-sided adhesive tape were attached to a microscope slide longitudinally leaving a blank space at the centre across which several $\sim$25 mm long fibres were mounted transversely. Fibre diameters were measured near the tapes where they were securely held.

The estimation of glass fibre diameters in air by the above procedure when only the graticule is used as the standard is subject to some inaccuracies arising from the large differences in the optical properties of the fibre *vis à vis* those of air. It is desirable to compare these measurements with those of other more accurate but slower methods in order to obtain appropriate calibration. The use of the scanning electron microscope for this purpose has been attempted[10] but in the present work two other methods were used.

It is easy to see that fibre diameters can be calculated if the density, weight and length of the fibre can be accurately determined. Single filaments of glass were pulled and wound on the drum of the fibre drawing apparatus described previously in five separate but consecutive bands, each band being the yield from 1 minute's pulling. During this exercise the furnace temperature just above the crucible was maintained at 1540°C and the drum was rotated at a constant speed of 6000 rpm. Utilising a value of 2.60 g cm^{-3} for the density of the filaments, obtained by the density gradient column method[10], the diameters of the fibres were computed from the measured weight and length of each band. The coefficients of variation for diameter measurements ranged from 0.75 to 1.9 per cent for individual bands.

The diameters of a large number of filaments from the above five bands were also measured using an interference fringe technique. The glass fibre was mounted transversely on a clean microscope slide and a 20 mm x 4 mm cover glass was placed on it with its length perpendicular to the fibre. A spring loaded pointed steel wire was screwed down on each end of the cover glass so that the cover glass arched over the fibre. The assembly was placed on the stage of a microscope and illuminated through the objective by light from a sodium lamp. A pattern of interference fringes was easily visible (Figure 1). Ensuring that the coverglass was in contact with the fibre (and this was aided by placing the fibre non-centrally with respect to the two pressure points) the lesser number of fringes between the fibre and the pressure point was counted using a low power objective. The experiment was repeated several times and the diameter of the fibre was calculated from the formula $d = n\lambda/2$ where n is the smallest number of fringes counted.

For filaments taken from the five bands a mean value of 9.06 μm was obtained for the diameter by the density method and 8.87 μm by the optical method. An average of these two values was used in obtaining the calibration for the routine measurements with the Watson image shearing eyepiece. It is important to note that calibration by the graticule overestimated glass fibre diameters by about 10 per cent.

The diameter of the asbestos fibre bundles was measured microscopically using the image shearing eyepiece. As the fibre bundle was very non-uniform in diameter along its length, it was necessary to design a special holder usable on the mechanical stage of the microscope, and provided with a facility by which the fibre bundles could be given a suitable amount of twist so that they had the appearance of a taut rope. Diameters were measured at selected points along the length of the fibre bundles where the visual edges were relatively free from imperfections. In general, six to ten measurements were made over a length of 2.5 mm.

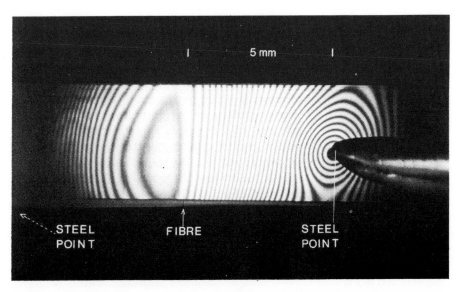

Figure 1 Interference fringe method of measuring fibre diameter

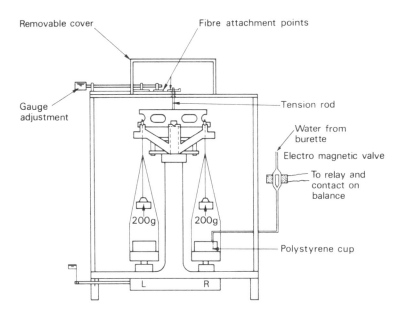

Figure 2 Fibre tensile testing apparatus

Fibre breaking load

Breaking loads in tension were measured using the Tecam microtensile testing instrument[11] and the apparatus developed by Gillett and Majumdar[12]. Each test on the Tecam machine took more than 15 minutes to perform and the other method which was considerably faster (less than 2 minutes per test) was preferred when a large number of fibres had to be tested.

The essential features of the instrument developed by Gillett and Majumdar are shown in Figure 2. A load applied to the balance pan is transferred by a rod set in the balance beam to the fibre mounted horizontally above the balance casing. The fibre is loaded by running water from a graduated burette through a flexible delivery tube into a polystyrene cup on the right balance pan. The rate of loading can be controlled by the jet size of the delivery tube when the burette tap is fully open. For the present work, a fibre gauge length of 5 mm was adopted and an electromagnetic valve was added which stopped the flow automatically when the fibre broke. When corroded glass fibres were tested using this apparatus, the tensile strength data showed a coefficient of variation of 5 per cent or less.

The instrument was calibrated by mounting a glass fibre horizontally in the usual way with weight varying from 5 to 20 g suspended from it. This was achieved by leading the fibre over a free running pulley wheel mounted on the apparatus. This calibration agreed well with that computed from the relative moments about the pivot. The Tecam machine was calibrated in accordance with the procedure described in the manufacturer's handbook.

When glass fibres from the same batch were tested by both machines, it was observed that the strength results from the Tecam were consistently lower, by up to $\sim$20 per cent. It should be pointed out here that in the use of this machine the fibres have to be handled with great

care and they are also exposed to temperatures exceeding 200°C when they are cemented to the anvils. Furthermore, compared to the other machine, the strain rate in the Tecam is considerably lower. It is likely that these factors are responsible for the observed discrepancy in the results obtained by the two methods.

The breaking loads for asbestos fibres were measured on the Tecam machine using the bundles which were previously employed in diameter measurements and which were still in the form of a taut rope.

Young's modulus of glass fibres

With the Tecam machine it is possible to measure directly the extension suffered by the fibre under load. The Young's modulus values of glass fibres, both in the corroded and uncorroded state, were derived from the results obtained with this machine.

Composite modulus of rupture

The modulus of rupture of the composite was calculated, using homogeneous beam theory, from the load data obtained with 150 mm x 50 mm x 9 mm specimens which were tested in four-point bending on an Instron machine.

RESULTS AND DISCUSSION
Glass fibre cement

The results of the various corrosion experiments relevant to the durability of glass fibre cement composites are shown in Figures 3 to 6. From Figure 3 it is seen that at ambient temperatures glass fibres lost significant proportions of their ultimate tensile strength (UTS) in course of the first 6 months when kept continuously in contact with Portland cement extracts. However, there is a firm indication that no further reduction in strength occurred up to 2 years at the end of which a UTS of $\sim$1300 N mm^{-2} was recorded. The Young's modulus of the fibres remained virtually unchanged throughout the entire period suggesting that the structure of the bulk glass is not affected in a major way as a result of reactions with the cement extract.

At 65°C a similar trend in durability is also observed (Figure 4) but in this case, as would be expected, the initial reduction in strength was more pronounced and after 14 days digestion glass fibres lost nearly two thirds of their pristine strength. Again, there is a strong indication that a stable UTS value of the order of 500 N mm⁻² was reached after about a month. As expected, this value is considerably lower than the corresponding strength at ambient temperatures. The Young's modulus of the fibres also shows a slight reduction after prolonged exposure to the alkaline cement extracts at the higher temperature. It should be pointed out that the strength data presented in Figures 3 and 4 were obtained with fibres which were employed previously in chemical corrosion studies[8]. These fibres had undergone several stages of mechanical handling and chemical processing and it is conceivable that during these operations the surface of the fibres was 'damaged' to a certain extent. This may partially account for the very substantial initial loss suffered by the fibres as depicted in Figures 3 and 4. From these results, however, it is not possible to judge the time when such a reduction in strength first manifested itself as the earliest measurements of the strength of reacted fibres at 20°C were carried out after 6 months. It is interesting to note in this connection that Oakley and Proctor[5] have recently reported that the tensile strengths of strands of glass fibres of composition similar to that used in the present study are reduced

from values in the range 1450 to 1750 N mm⁻² to 1200 to 1300 N mm⁻² after 24h in a cement environment. Allowing for the expected differences in the strength of the strand compared with that of single filaments, these results are in accord with those shown in Figure 3.

Cohen and Diamond[13] have recently reported that when placed in a 'cement effluent solution'[3] at ambient temperatures, alkali-resistant glass fibre strand made in their laboratory was weakened only slightly over a period of some weeks. The authors speculated that the long-term strength of these fibres could be about 80 per cent of the original values. These results are at variance with the results in Figure 3 and the observation made by Oakley and Proctor[5] mentioned earlier with respect to the change in the strength of the glass fibre during the initial period of their life in the cement environment. It may be pointed out that the original strength of the fibre strand used by Cohen and Diamond was very low at 940 N mm⁻² and it is certainly arguable that a much higher pristine strength might have shown a trend similar to that of Figure 3 bearing in mind that glass filaments in the latter case were not externally coated as must have been the case with the strands used by Cohen and Diamond.

Cohen and Diamond rightly point out that the rate of fibre strength loss at say 50°C cannot be used in any speculation on glass fibre properties at room temperature. As far as the zirconosilicate glasses (of the type discussed here) are concerned, a detailed recent

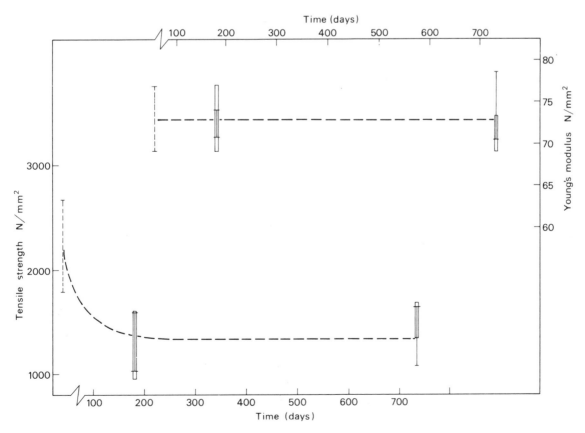

Figure 3 Tensile strength and Young's modulus of glass fibres reacted with cement extracts at 20°C. ┠──┨ pristine fibre; ┠───┨ fibre from OPC 737 extract; ▭ fibre from OPC 739 extract. The bars include ± one standard deviation

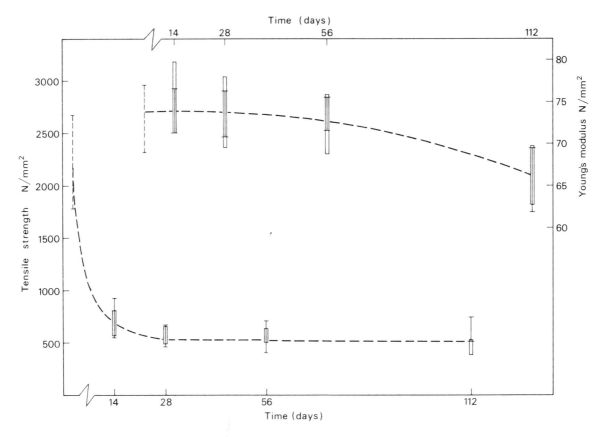

Figure 4 Tensile strength and Young's modulus of glass fibres reacted with cement extracts at 65°C. ⊢ — ⊣pristine fibre; ⊢——⊣ fibre from OPC 737 extract; ▭fibre from OPC 739 extract. The bars include ± one standard deviation

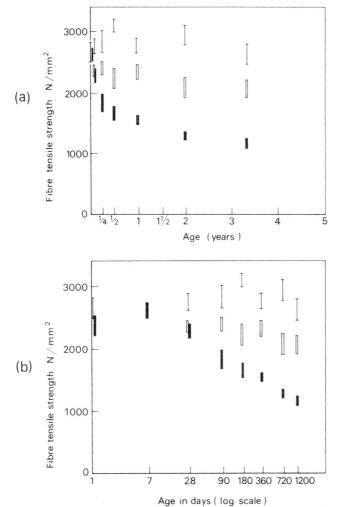

(a)

(b)

Figure 5 Tensile strength of alkali resistant glass fibres extracted from cement composites.
⊢——⊣control (chopped fibre); ▭fibres from air stored composite; ▬ fibres from water stored composite.

Figures 5a and 5b show the same strength results plotted against time and log time respectively. The bars represent 90% confidence limits

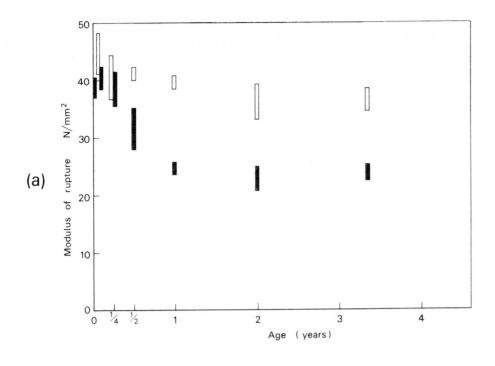

(a)

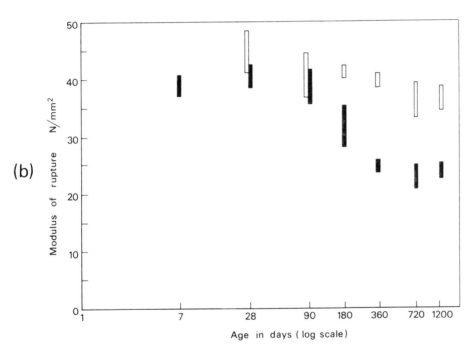

(b)

Figure 6 Modulus of rupture of cement composites containing alkali-resistant glass fibre.
⟍⟍⟍ air stored composite; ▬▬ water stored composite.

Figures 6a and 6b show the same strength results plotted against time and log time respectively. The bars represent 90% confidence limits

study[8] has shown that even at ambient temperatures ionic species are leached out of the fibres at a measurable rate. Some proposals have also been made in relation to the mechanism of glass/cement interactions for these glasses. However, it is not possible to predict the strength of glass fibres from these kinetic data as this is controlled mainly by the statistics of the size, population and distribution of the flaws in the fibre.

That alkali attack can promote serious reductions in the strength of glass fibres is demonstrated in several studies on E-glass fibres[6],[13] and by the observations that fibres

made from A-glass become powdery after prolonged exposure to an alkaline environment. Zirconosilicate glasses are inherently   alkali-resistant and once these glasses had been fiberised it was discovered that this property could be utilised successfully for the reinforcement of highly alkaline cements.

The tensile strength of Cem-FIL glass fibres after their removal from cement composite boards stored in air and under water over various periods of time is shown in Figure 5. It should be noted that in this experiment, some of the fibres remained firmly attached to the

39

matrix and tended to break into shorter lengths during removal and, therefore, only a small proportion of these fibres were long enough for strength testing. The remaining fibres comprising mainly the interior of the fibre bundles were affected to a lesser extent in this respect.

For comparison, the modulus of rupture values obtained with glass fibre cement from which fibres were removed for testing, are plotted in Figure 6, against the duration of storage of the composite specimens in the two environments mentioned above. The effect on fibre tensile strength of environment and time (Figure 5) is reflected in the properties of the composite (Figure 6). The physical basis for the strength time relationships, however, remains unknown for the time being and for this reason, and to avoid bias in interpretation, both logarithmic and linear time scales have been used to present the data in Figures 5 and 6.

The Young's modulus of the fibres extracted from the composite boards was not affected significantly by the prolonged exposure to two different environments. There was also no noticeable effect of these factors on the diameter of the fibre. In these respects the properties of the fibres removed from composites were very similar to those of fibres reacted with Portland cement extracts at ambient temperatures.

Cohen and Diamond[13] have also carried out similar experiments with cement composites using alkali resistant fibres from an American source. They removed fibres from composite specimens stored in air at 22°C and 50 per cent rh and measured their strength after various periods of ageing and observed that no reduction in strength had taken place. Unfortunately, not all their results were obtained from the same composite board. The corresponding results of the present investigation also obtained with specimens kept in air (but at 20°C and 40 per cent rh) show a small reduction in the strength of the fibres over a period of 3 to 4 years. Therefore, it can be said that there is a qualitative agreement between the two sets of results although the magnitude of fibre strength measured in the two lab-

oratories are very different. The long-term flexural strengths of the composites studied by Cohen and Diamond are, however, rather low, ~ 5 N mm^{-2}, and arguably this value is not much higher than that of the matrix. In that case it is difficult to see how the constancy of strength at this level with time can be cited as evidence for the lack of deterioration in the fibre.

In the present study, fibres extracted from water-stored composites showed a considerable reduction in strength with time (Figure 5). When stored under water the cement phase undergoes continuous hydration releasing, proportionately, much higher volumes of alkaline solution as well as crystalline Ca(OH)$_2$ and C–S–H 'gels' than is possible during curing in air of normal humidities. (In the latter case, even after several years, much of the cement remains unhydrated.) Thus the observed reduction in fibre strength may well be due to the combined action of the solution and the solid phases.

Finally, it should be mentioned that work in this laboratory suggests that in water storage conditions, composites made from alkali-resistant glass fibres are more durable with aluminous and other cements less alkaline than their Portland cement counterparts.

Asbestos cement

The strength values for asbestos fibre bundles presented in Figure 7 are considerably lower than those reported by other workers. For instance, Aveston[14] gives values of 3000 to 4400 N mm^{-2} for the UTS of chrysotile asbestos. Klos on the other hand, has quoted a range of 560 to 750 N mm^{-2} in a recent review[15] for chrysotile used commercially in the asbestos cement industry. As mentioned in a previous section the measurement of diameter of asbestos fibre bundles poses very serious problems. Aveston estimated the diameters of the 'fibres' from the known density of the fibre and weighing a quantity of it on a very sensitive microbalance. Such a method could not be used in the present case for the following reasons:

1 the fibres used in the commercial boards were not of

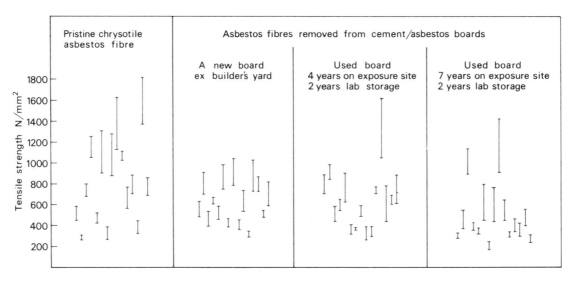

Figure 7 Tensile strength of asbestos fibres. Fibre bundles twisted to form a 'taut rope' before measurement of diameter. Bars represent values based on minimum to average diameters

one type but consisted of a mixture of blue and white asbestos,

2 the fibres could not be freed completely from the adherent matrix and,

3 the length of the fibre used on the Tecam machine was so short that a microbalance of very great sensitivity would have been required for weighing the fibre lengths. Such an instrument was not available. Instead an attempt was made at obtaining a realistic figure for the diameter of the fibre bundle by direct measurement.

In the present study, the change in the strength of the fibre bundles with time, on a relative rather than absolute basis, was the more important information to gather. In this respect, the values in Figure 7 suggest that as the asbestos cement gets older in use, the fibre strength might show a small decrease. The scatter in the data in Figure 7 is such that it is not possible to be precise about the extent of this decrease. From these values of asbestos fibre strength at various ages, it will be expected that the tensile and flexural strengths of asbestos cement sheets do not suffer significant reductions with age. Such a conclusion was reached by Jones[16] with respect to the modulus of rupture of asbestos cement roofing sheets exposed to weathering.

Very recently, Opoczky and Pentek[17] have examined some very old (up to 58 years) asbestos cement sheets by mineralogical methods such as petrographic microscopy, differential thermal and thermogravimetric analyses. They have concluded that some chemical reactions between asbestos fibrils and hydrated cements take place under natural weathering conditions. There is no indication, however, that these 'corrosion' reactions which are aided by atmospheric CO_2 have any influence on the tensile strength of the fibre or the composite. The present work adds support to this view.

CONCLUSIONS

Glass fibres lose a proportion of their pristine strength when placed in a Portland cement environment. The factors responsible for this reduction remain unknown in precise terms but chemical attack by alkalies must be one of the more important ones. Recent studies confirm that the superior performance of zirconosilicate glass fibres as reinforcement for cements vis à vis other glasses is linked with the inherent alkali-resistance of this glass. At ambient temperatures glass fibres of this type are likely to possess long-term tensile strengths of the order of 1200 to 1300 N mm^{-2} when placed in cement environments.

Present evidence suggests that there is no significant reduction with time in the strength of the asbestos reinforcement in asbestos cement products.

ACKNOWLEDGEMENT

A part of this work was supervised by Dr K Speakman before he left BRS. The tachometer circuit was devised by Dr R C De Vekey.

REFERENCES

1 **Biryukovich K L, Biryukovich Yu L and Biryukovich D L.** Glass-fibre reinforced cement. Kiev, Budivelmik, 1964. Civil Eng Res Assoc, London, 1965, Trans No 12.

2 **Allen H G.** Glass-fibre reinforced cement strength and stiffness. Con Ind Res and Inform Assoc, London, 1975, Report No 55.

3 **Majumdar A J and Ryder J F.** Glass Technol, 1968, **4** 78.

4 **Ali M A, Majumdar A J and Singh B.** J Mater Sci, 1975, **10** 1732.

5 **Oakley D R and Proctor B A.** Proc RILEM Symp, Fibre Reinforced Cement and Concrete, London, 1975. The Construction Press, 1975, 347–359.

6 **Majumdar A J and Nurse R W.** Mater Sci and Eng, 1974, **15** 107.

7 **De Vekey R C and Majumdar A J.** J Sci Instrum, 1967, **44** 864.

8 **Larner L J, Speakman K and Majundar A J.** J Non-Cryst Solids, 1976, **20** 43.

9 **Majumdar A J.** Proc RILEM Symp, Fibre Reinforced Cement and Concrete, London, 1975. The Construction Press, 1975, 279-313.

10 **Oakley D R.** Pilkington Bros, private communication, 1975.

11 **Marsh D M.** J Sci Instrum, 1961, **38** 229.

12 **Gillett R S and Majumdar A J.** Apparatus for testing tensile strengths of corroded glass fibres. BRS Current Paper CP 26/68.

13 **Cohen E B and Diamond S.** Proc RILEM Symp, Fibre Reinforced Cement and Concrete, London, 1975. The Construction Press, 1975, 315–325.

14 **Aveston J.** J Mater Sci, 1969, **4** 625.

15 **Klos H G.** Proc RILEM Symp, Fibre Reinforced Cement and Concrete, London, 1975. The Construction Press, 1975, 259–267.

16 **Jones F E.** Weathering tests on asbestos-cement roofing materials. London, HMSO, 1947. Building Research Technical Paper No 29.

17 **Opoczky L and Pentek L.** Proc RILEM Symp, Fibre Reinforced Cement and Concrete, London, 1975. The Construction Press, 1975, 269–276.

A study of the properties of Cem-FIL/OPC composites (CP 38/76)

Building Research Establishment and Pilkington Brothers Limited

Several important properties of glass reinforced cement composites, such as strength and elastic modulus, shrinkage, creep and fatigue, density, permeability and thermal expansion, and fire resistance, are described. The matrix considered is either neat ordinary Portland cement (OPC) paste or cement and sand mixtures.

Results up to 5 years are presented for composites containing five per cent by weight Cem-FIL glass fibres in neat OPC pastes in three different environments, and these have been used to predict the 20-year values of various mechanical properties.

FOREWORD

Alkali-resistant glass fibre is an invention of the Building Research Establishment that has been developed by Pilkington Brothers Limited under a licence granted by the National Research Development Corporation and marketed by Pilkington as Cem-FIL* fibre.

When this fibre is incorporated in cement or mortar matrices a composite material is obtained which has wide potential for non-structural and quasi-structural applications in the building industry and elsewhere. From 1969 onwards an extensive study of the properties of this composite material has been made by Pilkington and BRE under collaborative agreement.

This scientific report has been agreed by Pilkington and BRE and contains a summary of the main test results that are available from the initial series of glass fibre cement (GRC) boards made at BRE some 6 years ago and tested at BRE at regular periods after exposure to different environmental conditions. It should be noted that the majority of the results refer to GRC of a single formulation, namely five per cent by weight of Pilkington's Cem-FIL AR glass fibre in ordinary Portland cement matrix and prepared by the spray-suction method which was developed at BRE; it also covers some results obtained by Pilkington on composites with matrices containing sand.

A variety of mix formulations and production techniques can be developed for GRC to give composites with widely different performance characteristics to suite a range of applications. For this reason, and because they have the necessary expertise in manufacture, quality control, application and design, Pilkington should be consulted on all applications of GRC.

D F CORNELIUS
23 December 1975

*Registered trademark of Fibreglass Limited

LIST OF PROPERTIES QUOTED IN TEXT, WITH ABBREVIATIONS

From tension tests
> Ultimate tensile strength (UTS)
> Bend-over point (BOP)
> Strain-to-failure
> Fatigue life
> Young's modulus

From bending tests
> Modulus of rupture (MOR)
> Limit of proportionality (LOP)
> Creep strain
> Stress rupture behaviour
> Fatigue life

From other tests
> Izod impact strength
>
> Across-plane compressive strength
> In-plane compressive strength
>
> Inter-laminar shear strength(ILS)
> In-plane shear strength
> Punch-through shear strength
>
> Shrinkage strains
> Thermal expansion and conductivity
> Air and water vapour permeance
> Fire properties
> Density

INTRODUCTION

Glass reinforced cement composites (GRC) can provide a whole range of materials, each one having its own properties dependent on the matrix used, the method of manufacture, age, environment and fibre content. The first development and assessment of GRC, at the Building Research Establishment, was based on essentially neat cement paste matrices: the most extensive property and durability data exist for these types of materials and the results therefrom, given below and summarised in Table 1 are considered representative of the characteristics of well made GRC*.

With all composite materials it is necessary to sample and test the actual material used in component manufacture. This is a necessary requirement with all GRC, and is even more particularly needed when changes have been made to the matrix formulation, the fabrication or the spraying method.

One of the most important objectives of early GRC research work was the provision of basic information

---

*Present commercial practice is to include approximately 25 per cent by weight of fine sand to reduce shrinkage strains and improve dimensional stability - see also Table 3. It is not thought that this sand addition will invalidate the general conclusions on durability given in this document.

on the long-term durability of OPC/glass fibre systems. Initially this was to be based on measurements of simple bending strength (modulus of rupture) and impact (Izod type); air, water and natural weather storage were taken as examples of possible working conditions. Subsequently, after the first 'standard' samples were manufactured and placed in store, it was seen to be increasingly necessary to augment the above data with measurements of tensile properties and the limit of proportionality in bending, and to lay more emphasis on exposure to natural weather.

The long-term durability assessment given below is based on results from four boards (water:cement ratio 0.28 to 0.33) made by the spray-dewatering process and containing 5 per cent by weight of 34 mm long chopped strands of Cem-FIL and with matrices of OPC and OPC plus 10 per cent fine sand, both with and without a small addition of ligno-sulphonate flow additive. After spraying and dewatering, the boards were stored for 24 hours under wet hessian and then cured under polythene for 6 days at normal laboratory temperatures. They were then cut (wet) into samples and transferred to the appropriate storage conditions.

These boards provide the most comprehensive and consistent comparison of properties across all three storage conditions, extending to 5 years with some omissions in tensile data. From these data, estimates have been made of the likely long-term property values (at an age of 20 years). These estimates have been based on the understanding which has so far been built up of GRC behaviour, on visual extrapolation of graphs and on the results of statistically based curve fitting investigations.

Other GRC properties such as creep, fatigue, compressive strength, shear strength and shrinkage have also been considered together with some results on the effect of sand additions on GRC strength properties. These data have been obtained from experiments with separate boards.

GENERAL MATERIAL BEHAVIOUR AND AGEING CHARACTERISTICS

The tensile stress-strain curves shown in Figure 1, illustrate the basic early-life loadbearing and failure behaviour of 'standard' spray-suction dewatered GRC containing about 5 per cent (green weight) of 38 mm chopped strands of Cem-FIL fibre. An initial approximately linear portion, with the Young's modulus of the cement matrix, is followed by a relatively sharp bend-over to a nearly horizontal region in which fine and multiple cracking develops throughout the sample.

The fine cracking above the bend-over point (BOP) absorbs considerable amounts of energy resulting in high impact strength and tough behaviour with an ability to relieve local stress concentrations. In bending tests there is a redistribution of stress across the section of the sample and the modulus of rupture, as calculated by simple theory, is about two and a half times the ultimate tensile strength (UTS). The stress level at which

Table 1 Strength properties of spray-dewatered OPC/GRC at various ages (5 per cent glass fibre), BRE data

		Total range for air and water storage conditions at 28 days	1 Year			5 Years			20 Years (estimated)	
			Air*	Water†	Weathering	Air*	Water†	Weathering	Air*	Water†
a) Bending MOR	(MN/m^2)	35-50	35-40	22-25	30-36	30-35	21-25	21-23	26-34	20-25
LOP	(MN/m^2)	14-17	9-13	16-19	14-17	10-12	16-19	15-18	8-10	16-18
b) Tensile UTS	(MN/m^2)	14-17	14-16	9-12	11-14	13-15	9-12	7-8	12-15	8-11
BOP	$(MN/m2)$	9-10	7-8	9-11	9-10	7-8	7-9	7-8	7-8	8-11
Young's modulus	(GN/m^2)	20-25	20-25	28-34	20-25	20-25	28-34	25-32	20-25	28-34
c) Impact strength (Izod)	Nmm/mm^2	17-31	18-25	8-10	13-16	18-21	4-6	4-7	14-20	4-7

*At 40 per cent relative humidity and 20^oC
† At $18\text{-}20^oC$

marked departure from linearity (LOP) occurs in a bending test is also raised noticeably (Figure 2) above the tensile bend-over point.

Present durability data, given in more detail below, indicate that, in dry storage conditions, modulus of rupture, tensile strength and strain to failure remain high but there is a fall in LOP and BOP levels. On the other hand on storage in wet conditions (eg, one year in water, or five years in natural weathering) GRC becomes essentially brittle (Figure 3); the tensile stress-strain curve terminates just beyond the bend-over point. The MOR reduces considerably and it nearly meets the LOP value. However, LOP and Young's modulus both increase somewhat in these conditions (Figure 2).

The two different levels of bend-over point shown in Figure 1 reflect some non-randomness in fibre orientation in these boards. This orientation factor affects UTS, BOP and MOR values but makes little difference to LOP or Young's modulus. Results quoted subsequently are for longitudinal samples.

Curve fitting and extrapolation
In dry air storage, changes in strength occur slowly and are relatively small; in water immersion conditions there is a rapid fall in strength which then remains almost constant over one to five years. In both cases it is possible to make reasonable, if approximate, extrapolations of the test data available in order to predict longer-term properties, as indicated in the Introduction.

In temperate natural weathering conditions the loss in strength takes place over the full experimental time-scale and considerably more interpretation and judgment is required in making even very approximate predictions of long-term properties: visual extrapolation of the data plotted on a linear (actual) time axis can lead to widely differing estimates, and mathematical extrapolation requires first that the form of the strength/time relationship be known.

The factors that lead to the change with time in composite properties are not fully understood, and no theoretical method for determining the shape of the durability curve exists at present.

The shape of the strength/time curves suggests two simple empirical relationships that might reasonably describe the experimental data. In this present work, empirical curve fitting and extrapolation has been carried out using these two relationships:

1   a logarithmic relationship, ie $S = a - b \log t$
2   an exponential relationship, ie $S = a + be^{-ct}$

The extrapolation on a logarithmic time-base assumes that any changes in properties that have occurred in the short period over which measurements have been made will continue throughout the whole of the longer-term period in question, but at a decreasing real-time rate until a lower limit, or 'cut-off', set by the properties of the 'matrix' (OPC plus degraded fibres) is eventually reached. In this method of extrapolation the slope of the linear extrapolation on the logarithmic time-scale is heavily influenced by the changes in the early years, although the mechanism or the rate of these early changes may not necessarily be relevant to the longer-term ageing mechanisms.

Extrapolation on an exponential basis implies that an equilibrium condition is reached, and that the 20-year value, estimated from the curve fitting, is essentially asymptotic to a stable value. This implies the expectation that the changes in natural weathering conditions will resemble those in water immersion, albeit at a considerably lower rate. It implies also that the effect of other factors unique to the natural weathering condition, eg cyclic temperature and moisture conditions, is small.

The essential difference between the two methods of estimating the 20-year data is that although both assume that the rate of deterioration decreases with real time (an assumption which is amply supported by experimental data), the exponential method implies that it will stop altogether whereas the logarithmic method implies that the strength will continue to decline, albeit at an ever decreasing rate, until the 'matrix' level is reached.

There is not at present sufficient evidence to indicate clearly which of the two mathematical relationships provides the more accurate description of the results in natural weathering and in this report 20-year values estimated by both methods are presented (Table 2). Experimental data are plotted on both logarithmic and linear time-scales.

Measurement and prediction of tensile strength

Although careful attempts have been made to measure the ultimate tensile strength (UTS) of specimens aged under dry, wet and natural weather conditions, it is universally recognised that it is very difficult to make such measurements on brittle materials. Any departure from 'perfect' experimental conditions (eg misalignment, stress concentration at grips, etc) will inevitably lead to an underestimate of the UTS. This becomes particularly important with GRC after embrittlement in wet or weather storage.

Ultimate tensile strength is an important design parameter for certain component structures, so it is important that an attempt be made to estimate 'true' long-term values. With samples of GRC aged in dry and

in water immersion conditions there is experimental evidence which indicates that the UTS changes with ageing in a way that roughly parallels the MOR, and that the ratio of MOR to UTS is about 2.5:1 for all ages beyond the very early stages of cure. In these experiments it was only in the case of the samples aged under natural weather conditions that average MOR/UTS ratios of up to 3:1 were observed, suggesting that for such specimens the direct measurement of UTS was particular difficult — possibly due to warping of specimens which increased with age under these conditions. Also only a few samples were available for the tensile tests after this prolonged ageing.

For this reason the natural weather UTS values given in Table 2 have been estimated in two ways:

(i) from direct measurement on simple strip specimens, and

(ii) from MOR measurements divided by 2.5

with extrapolations in each case made by both logarithmic and exponential methods.

While a direct measurement of UTS is obviously preferable, in the case of the naturally weathered samples there is some doubt that 'perfect' experimental conditions were achieved, and the number of measurements was small. In this case despite the uncertanties of the indirect empirical approach (ii), it probably gives the better estimate of the 'true' material tensile strength.

MECHANICAL PROPERTIES IN AIR STORAGE CONDITIONS

Figures 4, 5 and 6 show the variations of MOR and LOP, UTS and BOP, and Izod impact strength (respectively) over a five-year period. Material was stored in controlled 40 per cent humidity conditions at temperatures of $18^{\circ}C$ for the first two years and $20^{\circ}C$ for the remainder of the time. The four-point bending tests were carried out on specimens of 150 mm x 50 mm x 9 mm over a

Table 2 Estimated strength properties of spray-dewatered OPC/GRC (5 per cent glass fibre) after 20 years' exposure to temperate natural weather, BRE data

Bending properties (MN/m^2)				Tensile properties (MN/m^2)						Young's modulus GN/m^2	Impact strength (Izod) Nmm/mm^2
MOR		LOP		UTS Direct measurement*		UTS Estimated**		BOP (Governed by UTS value)			
Log†	Exp††	Log	Exp	Log	Exp	Log	Exp	Log	Exp		
12 - 15	21 - 23	12 - 15	15 - 18	4 - 6	7 - 10	5 - 6	8.5 - 9.5	4 - 6* 5 - 6**	7 - 10* 8.5 - 9.5**	25 - 32	2 - 6

NOTES.

*Taken from tensile test results on strip specimens - possibly an underestimate
**An estimation of UTS from MOR data ie UTS = MOR/2.5 - not an absolute parameter but there is supporting experimental evidence
See Section on Measurement and prediction of tensile strength

† Log = Logarithmic extrapolation of data - assumes continual decay throughout the 20 years
†† Exp = Exponential extrapolation - assumes equilibrium values achieved with 20 years
See Section on Curve fitting and extrapolation

total span of 135 mm. The tensile tests used simple strip specimens of the same size and the impact tests were carried out on the broken halves of the flexural specimens.

Under these dry storage conditions there is seen to be a small fall in strength properties in the early years but the material retains its tough pseudo-ductile behaviour at five years (see also Figure 3). On the basis of present trends best estimates of average strength properties at (say) 20 years are MOR 26 to 34 MN/m^2, UTS 12 to 15 MN/m^2, impact 14 to 20 Nmm/mm^2.

Figure 4 shows a fall in LOP values over the first one to two years in these conditions; this seems to stabilise at about 50 to 60 per cent of its initial value and a best estimate for a 20-year value would be about 8 to 10 MN/m^2, BOP would be 7 to 8 MN/m^2 at 20 years. (Figure 5).

Temperature effects
A small specific investigation of the effects of dry storage at elevated temperatures on the bending properties, has been conducted. After the initial seven-day cure period specimens were stored in ovens at 25^oC, 35^oC, 40^oC and 50^oC for up to two years. The results, given in Figures 8 and 9 indicate that temperatures up to 35^oC have little effect on MOR. Temperatures up to 50^oC have little effect on LOP and impact values up to 2 years.

Humidity effects
At 40 per cent relative humidity (RH) and 20^oC, there is only a small fall in strength properties over five years as shown in Figures 4, 5 and 6. In a comparative experiment illustrated by Figure 7 for the MOR it has been shown that an increase of the humidity causes a systematic increase in the rate of strength loss of GRC made with neat cement paste. At 90 per cent RH, the rate of strength loss is similar to the rate in water storage.

At and above 60 per cent RH (at 20^oC) there is little change of LOP with time whereas at 40 per cent RH there may be a fall of up to 50 per cent (Figure 7).

Results obtained with samples stored in a normally centrally-heated working laboratory with variable humidity and temperature, showed a very similar pattern to the 40 per cent RH storage conditions.

The strength properties of GRC containing 30 per cent sand at various humidities appear similar to those of composites made with neat cement up to 90 days (Figure 7).

At elevated temperatures and high humidities GRC suffers a rapid fall in strength initially. At 50^oC and 60 to 70 per cent RH GRC made with neat OPC gave a MOR value of 16 to 19 MN/m^2 in less than 30 days but maintained this level up to 60 days.

MECHANICAL PROPERTIES IN WATER STORAGE CONDITIONS
The variations in MOR and LOP, UTS and BOP and Izod impact strength over a five-year period are shown in Figures 10, 11 and 12 respectively. Samples were stored immersed in water at 18^oC for the first two years and thereafter at 20^oC. These results, together with the strain to failure data in Figure 3, showed embrittlement and strength loss over the first year with subsequent stabilisation at approximately constant values. On the other hand there is a small increase in LOP values in these conditions.

Although the stress-strain curve obtained with simple strip-type tensile tests on wet aged material indicates almost entirely brittle behaviour, there remains a very small bend-over region. The MOR also remained somewhat above LOP (Figure 2), and MOR and impact strength values were about two to three times cement paste values.

On the basis of present results and trends the best estimates of 20-year values would be MOR 20 to 25 MN/m^2, LOP 16 to 18 MN/m^2, UTS 8 to 11 MN/m^2, impact 4 to 7 Nmm/mm^2. Bend-over point stress levels would be indistinguishable from UTS values.

Temperature effects
Present results show that increases in the temperature of water storage cause more rapid and more severe losses in strength of GRC. The magnitude and extent of these effects is shown in Figures 13, 14 and 15. At 50^oC the MOR is seen to merge completely with the LOP at three months, indicating a more complete embrittlement than at the lower water storage temperatures.

MECHANICAL PROPERTIES IN NATURAL WEATHERING CONDITIONS
Results obtained with naturally weathered samples exposed in a horizontal position at BRS are shown in Figures 16, 17 and 18. Over the five-year period, air temperatures on the site varied from -10^oC to 31^oC, relative humidity from 30 to 100 per cent and the average annual rainfall was about 590 mm. The material was weathered as pre-cut 150 mm x 50 mm x 9 mm test coupons but other results over one to two years' weathering indicate no difference between the behaviour of horizontal, vertical or sloping exposed sheets.

The results given in Figures 16, 17 and 18 show that the strength properties have fallen more slowly than in water storage conditions over the five-year period, but they have reached approximately the same levels at the end of that period and appear to be still falling although the relatively few samples tested after three years make it difficult to give a firm conclusion at present.

Bearing in mind both the effect of temperature on results in water storage (Figures 13, 14 and 15), and the tendency of GRC properties to level out in total immersion conditions at a constant temperature, it seems reasonable to assume that the natural weathering results will follow the same pattern and level out somewhere below the 18 to 20°C water strength levels, at values corresponding to the average temperature of exposure to wet conditions.

With the limited data and the longer time-scales involved in these strength changes it is very much more difficult to make valid predictions of properties at 20 years than in the case of water storage. Adopting the approach outlined above, the long-term properties have been estimated by extrapolation of both logarithmic and exponential curves fitted to the five-year strength data. These results are presented in Table 2.

The LOP values remain stable in temperate weather conditions and the BOP becomes virtually coincident with the measured UTS after about two years.

Weathering data are also being accumulated on a range of sites in widely differing climatic conditions. After preliminary results at one year, two situations emerge as giving noticeably different results from the results of the tests carried out at BRS. In hot, wet conditions (Singapore) there is a very rapid drop in strength properties over the first six months with an indication of levelling out at one year. In Toronto, samples subjected to freeze-thaw conditions show signs of a fall in LOP level.

YOUNG'S MODULUS VALUES
Young's modulus is essentially a matrix-controlled property with values similar to that of cement paste. Tensile measurements have given results of 20 to 25 GN/m^2 in air at all ages up to five years, and values of 28 to 34 GN/m^2 after prolonged storage in wet conditions.

CREEP, STRESS RUPTURE AND FATIGUE BEHAVIOUR
Measurements of creep in bending and direct tension have been made for indoor and water storage conditions. In direct tension creep strains are very much smaller than expansion-contraction strains due to humidity changes.

The bending tests show that at all stress levels creep behaviour of composites is qualitatively similar to that of cement. At stresses less than the LOP the creep is in fact quantitatively the same as that of the matrix material alone when made under the same conditions and loaded at the same time. Figures 19 and 20 show the ratio of creep strain to initial strain for applied bending stresses below the LOP level for indoor and water storage, respectively, for various loading times. Most data are for a cement paste matrix with a water:cement ratio of 0.3 but also included in Figure 20 are results for a 1:2 sand cement mortar matrix with the same water: cement ratio showing a reduction in creep. This reduction may not however occur if the water:cement ratio is allowed to rise when adding the sand.

Stress rupture experiments under constant bending load

in water and indoor conditions have shown no failure below an applied stress level of 19.5 MN/m^2 in two years. In temperate weathering conditions there had been two stress rupture failures at 18 MN/m^2 at 18 months out of 12 samples at that stress level.

Repeated load fatigue tests have been carried out in bending and direct tension. The bending results show that lives of greater than 10^5 cycles are obtained in wet and dry conditions at the LOP stress (Figure 21) with lives in excess of 10^6 cycles at 10 MN/m^2. Direct tension tests show a life of about 2 x 10^4 cycles at the BOP and a life of 10^6 cycles or above at 4.5 MN/m^2 in both prolonged wet and dry storage conditions. Figure 22 shows results for two-year-old indoor stored material.

COMPRESSIVE AND SHEAR STRENGTHS
These properties are markedly direction-dependent and Figure 23 illustrates both the directions of test and the definitions used in this section.

Compressive strengths
The across-plane compressive strength of GRC is equal to that of cement paste at about 100 MN/m^2. There is no indication of a fall with time over six months' dry storage and in wet conditions this property would be expected to remain constant or to increase.

The in-plane compressive strength is somewhat lower at about 65 MN/m^2; again there is no indication of a fall after six months' dry storage and in wet conditions this matrix-controlled property would again be expected to remain constant or to increase.

Shear strengths
Inter-laminar shear strength is a matrix-controlled property. Initial values of about 2 MN/m^2 appear to remain constant in dry storage conditions and are a little higher in wet storage.

In-plane shear strength data are limited by lack of an entirely suitable test. Minimum values are 8 to 9 MN/m^2.

The punch-through shear test is a fibre-controlled property. Initial values are very close to those of MOR at 35 to 40 MN/m^2 and are expected to follow the same durability pattern as MOR in different environments.

EFFECT OF SAND ADDITIONS ON MECHANICAL PROPERTIES
In order to control shrinkage it is often desirable to include sand in composite matrices. Tests have been carried out with a series of GRC boards containing 5 per cent by weight glass fibre and having a range of sand contents. The boards were all made at Lathom with a nominal water:solids ratio of 0.26. Results after 7-day water cure and subsequent dry storage are shown in Figure 24. No marked changes in MOR, LOP, UTS or BOP are observed at sand:cement ratios up to at least 1:2. At higher sand contents a drop in all properties is

observed, probably due to increases in porosity or changes in the degree of hydration in these boards. At high sand levels there is a small improvement in strength with time in dry storage conditions and in water storage the strain to failure is retained for a little longer at these high sand contents. No changes in durability or strength levels ascribable to sand additions were observed for sand:cement ratios up to about 1:2 (up to one year in water and air).

SHRINKAGE

In common with other cement-bonded materials GRC undergoes drying shrinkage on exposure to low humidity/high temperature conditions. For neat cement the ultimate initial drying shrinkage can be up to 0.3 per cent at 50°C and 30 to 40 per cent RH. This shrinkage may be reduced by incorporating an aggregate such as a silica sand into the formulation and the ultimate shrinkage versus sand content curve is as shown in Figure 25. Up to 25 to 30 per cent by weight of sand, on the total mix (cement plus sand plus fibre plus water) can be easily incorporated into a typical mix.

THERMAL EXPANSION COEFFICIENTS, THERMAL CONDUCTIVITY AND GAS AND WATER VAPOUR PERMEABILITY OF GRC

The thermal expansion coefficient of dried GRC lies between 7 and 12×10^{-6} °K^{-1} but for damp material it may be as high as 36×10^{-6} °K^{-1} under certain conditions of atmospheric humidity.

The thermal conductivity of GRC depends more or less linearly on density of the composite and varies between 0.5 W (m °K)$^{-1}$ at a bulk density of 1.70 t m^{-3} and 1.1 to 1.3 W (m °K)$^{-1}$ at 2.20 t m^{-3}.

Various sorts of permeability of GRC may depend on material age, storage conditions and water cement ratio and the following observations have been made:

(a) air permeance increases with storage in dry (40 per cent RH) conditions: a value of 3 metric perms was recorded at one year with some further increase probably indicated by the trend

of results. In high humidity (90 per cent RH) and wet storage conditions permeance was < 0.15 metric perms.

(b) water vapour permeance values were 7 metric perms for a board made at 0.35 water:cement ratio, and fell slowly over one year. For a board made at 0.25 water:cement ratio the water vapour permeance was ⩽ 3 metric perms.

(c) GRC passes the ISO impermeability test at an age of 28 days.

DENSITY

Density of GRC materials, like all other properties, varies with fabrication conditions and matrix formulation. For direct spray materials values lie in the range 1.75 to 2.0 t m^{-3}; for spray-dewatered materials in the range 2.0 to 2.1 t m^{-3}.

PERFORMANCE IN FIRE

In assessing fire performance it must be remembered that GRC is not a single material but a range of materials whose properties depend upon the formulation and method of manufacture used. In designing components for fire protection it is therefore necessary to consider and test each formulation or design. Fire testing has been carried out to BS 476 Fire tests on building materials and structures, which comprises 6 parts: Parts 3 and 8 relate mainly to testing of structures, Parts 4 to 7 are relevant to the testing of materials.

When tested to Parts 4 to 6 of this standard, GRC composites with a neat cement matrix containing 5 per cent fibre and a small amount of organic plasticiser (up to 0.3 per cent w/w) have given excellent results, being designated:

Part 4 : 'Non-combustible'
Parts 5 and 6 : Initial index of performance $i_1 = 0.0$
Final index of performance $I = 0.0$

In indicative Fire Resistance tests (Part 8) suitably formulated GRC composites containing 5 per cent fibre

Table 3 Effect of sand additions on short-term properties of spray-dewatered GRC (5 per cent glass, 0.26 water:solids ratio) - PB data

Fraction of sand in dry mix wt %	Sand:cement ratio by wt	7 days MOR	7 days LOP (MN/m²)	7 days UTS	7 days BOP	28 days MOR	28 days LOP (MN/m²)	28 days UTS	28 days BOP
0	0	43	12	-	-	- -	.	15	8
10	0.11	40	12	-	-	-	-	14	8
20	0.25	42	15	-	-	-	-	14	8
32.8	0.48	38	11	-	-	-	-	15	8
40	0.66	33	10	-	-	-	-	13	7
50	1.0	26	7	-	-	-	-	11	5
60	1.5	14	5	-	-	-	-	8	3

have consistently satisfied the integrity requirement for a minimum of one hour. Performance may, however, be affected by long-term exposure to conditions which can bring about changes in the physical properties of the material. Where appropriate, testing can be carried out after accelerated ageing.

Full scale tests in accordance with Part 8 have been carried out on several GRC sandwich panel structures. The performance of such structures is strongly dependent on the nature of the core material employed. A two-hour rating has been readily achieved and in some cases a four-hour rating has been approached. Test certificates relating to particular panel designs are available.

It is possible to design GRC components, eg cladding panels, to meet specific fire requirements.

ACKNOWLEDGEMENTS

The work described in this paper forms part of the research programme of the Building Research Establishment of the Department of the Environment.

Since this programme of research was initiated some six years ago, a large number of people have contributed to it so it is not possible to acknowledge all of them here. However, mention should be made of the significant research contributions by Dr R W B Nurse, Dr A J Majumdar, Mr F J Grimer, Miss V Laws, Mr J F Ryder, Dr K Speakman, Mr R C DeVekey and Mr M A Ali of BRE, and by Dr E J Smith, Mr B A Proctor, Mr K L Litherland, Mr P Irlam, Mr D R Oakley and Mr J A Lee of Pilkington.

The research strategy was developed within the Steering/Liaison Committee which comprised the Building Research Establishment (Dr B R Steele, Mr D F Cornelius, Dr W H Gutt), Pilkington Brothers Limited (Dr L C F Blackman, Dr A G Tallentire) and the National Research Development Corporation. (Dr J G Waller).

The co-operation of Pilkington Brothers Limited in releasing their research results for publication is gratefully acknowledged.

BIBLIOGRAPHY

Ali, M A, Majumdar, A J and **Singh, B**. Properties of glass fibre cement — the effect of fibre length and fibre content. J Mater Sci, Vol 10, 1975, pp 1732-1740.

DeVekey, R G and **Majumdar, A J**. Interfacial bond strength of glass fibre reinforced cement composites, J Mater Sci, Vol 5, 1970, pp 183-184.

Grimer, F J and **Ali, M A**. The strengths of cements reinforced with glass fibres. Mag Conc Res, Vol 21, No 66, March 1969, pp 23-30.

Hibbert, A P and **Grimer, F J**. Flexural fatigue of glass fibre cement. J Mater Sci, Vol 10, 1975, pp 2124-2133.

Jaras, A C and **Litherland, K L**. Microstructural features in glass fibre reinforced cement composites. Fibre reinforced cement and concrete. RILEM Symposium 1975, pp 327-334. Construction Press Ltd.

Laws, V. The efficiency of fibrous reinforcement of brittle matrices. J Phys D, Appl Phys, Vol 4, 1971, pp 1737-1746.

Majumdar, A J and **Nurse, R W**. Glass fibre reinforced cement. Materials Science and Engineering, Vol 15, 1974, pp 107-127.

Majumdar, A J and **Ryder, J F**. Glass fibre reinforcement of cement products. Glass Technology, Vol 9, No 3, June 1968, pp 78-84.

Majumdar, A J and **Tallentire, A G**. Glass fibre reinforced cement-based materials. American Concrete Institute, SP-44, pp 351-362.

Nair, N G. Mechanics of glass fibre reinforced cement. Fibre reinforced cement and concrete, RILEM Symposium 1975, pp 81-93. Construction Press Ltd.

Oakley, D R and **Proctor, B A**. Tensile stress strain behaviour of glass fibre reinforced cement composites, Fibre reinforced cement and concrete, RILEM Symposium 1975, pp 347-359, Construction Press Ltd.

Proctor, B A. Glass fibre reinforced cement, Physics in Technology, Vol 6, Jan 1975, pp 28-32.

Proctor, B A, Oakley, D R and **Wiechers, W** Tensile stress/strain characteristics of glass fibre reinforced cement. Composites-Standards, Testing and Design. IPC Science and Technology Press, 1974, pp 106-107.

Steele, B R. Glass fibre reinforced cement. Proceedings International Building Exhibition Conference on Prospects for fibre reinforced materials, London, November 1971, published by BRE, 1972, pp 29-39.

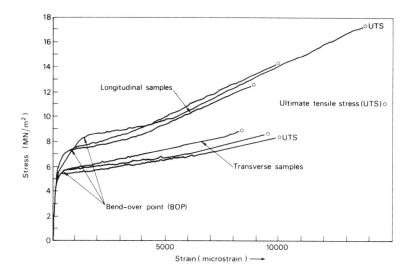

Figure 1 Tensile stress-strain curves for spray-dewatered GRC

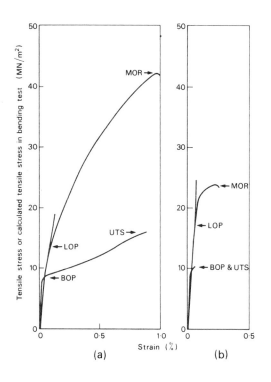

Figure 2 Representative stress-strain curves in tension and bending:

(a) After 28 days in water at 18°C to 20°C
(b) After 5 years in water at 18°C to 20°C

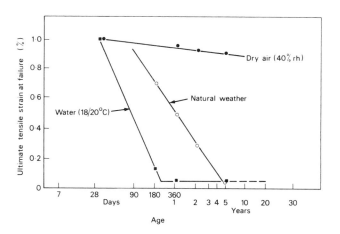

Figure 3 Strain-to-failure in tension for GRC at various ages in dry air, natural weather and water storage

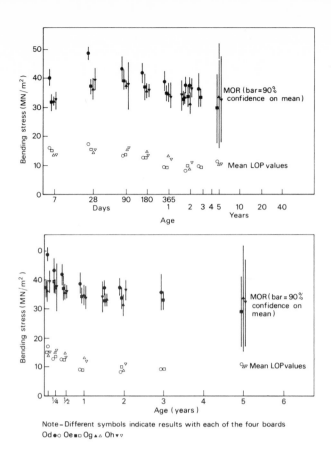

Figure 4 Modulus of rupture and limit of proportionality in bend for GRC stored in air at 18°C to 20°C and 40 per cent RH

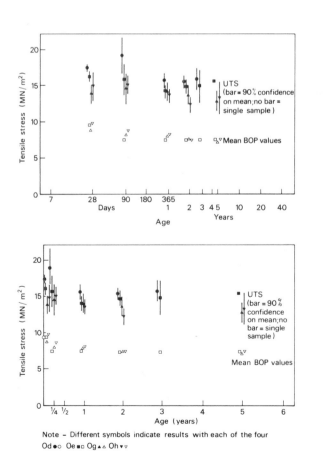

Figure 5 Ultimate tensile strength and bend-over point for GRC stored in air at 18°C to 20°C and 40 per cent RH

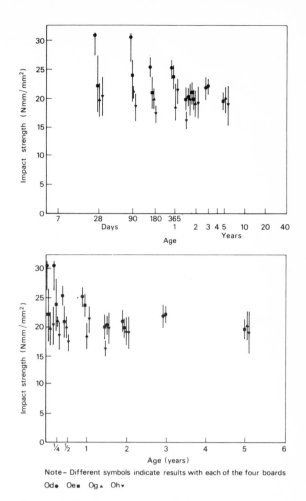

Figure 6 Izod impact strength for GRC stored in air at 18°C to 20°C and 40 per cent RH

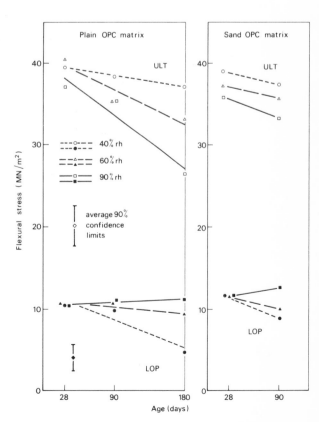

Figure 7 The effect of humidity on the flexural properties of GRC at 20°C

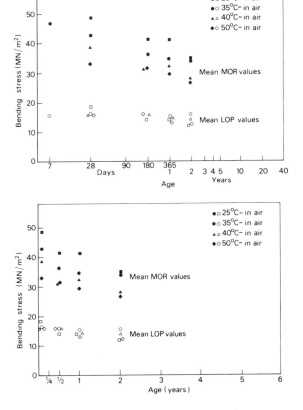

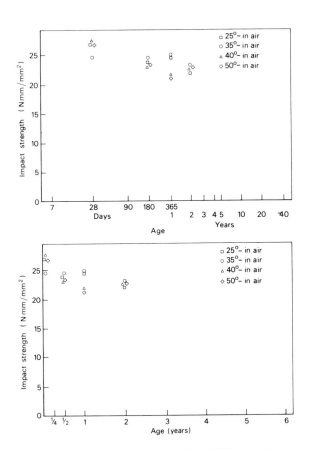

Figure 8 Modulus of rupture and limit of proportionality in bend for GRC stored in air at elevated temperatures (25°C to 50°C)

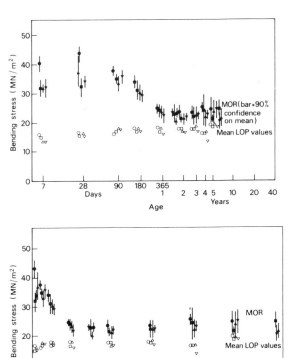

Figure 10 Modulus of rupture and limit of proportionality in bend for GRC stored in water at 18°C to 20°C

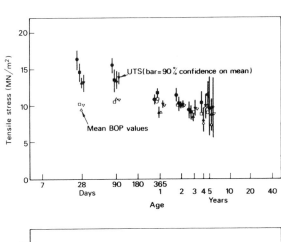

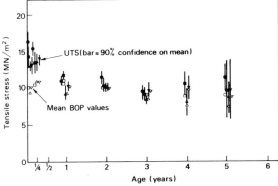

Figure 9 Izod impact strength for GRC stored in air at elevated temperatures (25°C to 50°C)

Figure 11 Ultimate tensile strength and bend-over point for GRC stored in water at 18°C to 20°C

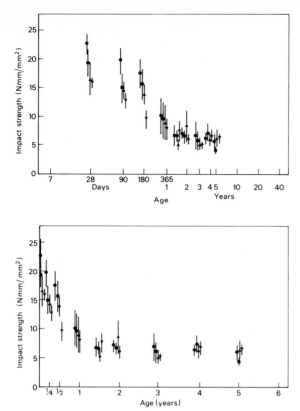

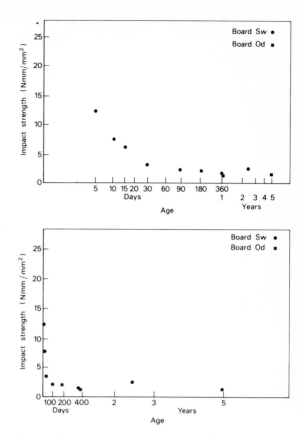

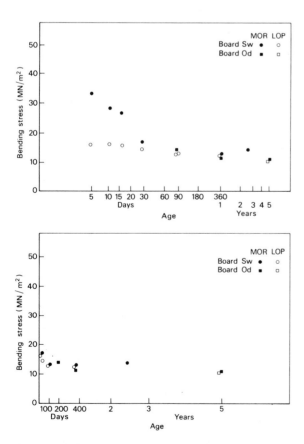

Note – Different symbols indicate results with each of the four boards
Od● Oe■ Og▲ Oh▼

Figure 12 Izod impact strength for GRC
stored in water at 18°C to 20°C

Figure 14 Izod impact strength for GRC
stored in water at 50°C

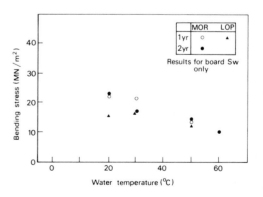

Figure 15 Modulus of rupture and limit of
proportionality in bend for GRC
stored for 1 to 2 years in water at
elevated temperatures (20°C to
60°C)

Figure 13 Modulus of rupture and limit of proportionality in bend for GRC stored in water
at 50°C

53

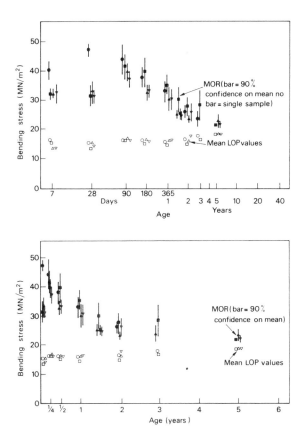

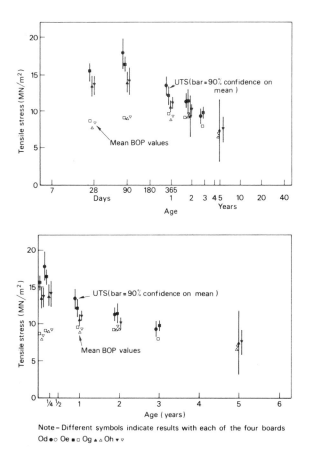

Figure 16 Modulus of rupture and limit of proportionality in bend for GRC stored in natural weather conditions in the UK

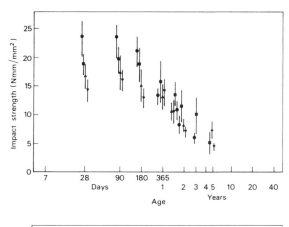

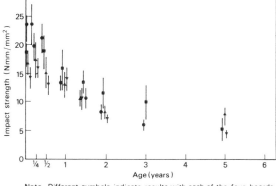

Figure 18 Izod impact strength for GRC stored in natural weather conditions in the UK

Note – Different symbols indicate results with each of the four boards
Od● Oe■ Og▲ Oh▼

Figure 17 Ultimate tensile strength and bend-over point for GRC stored in natural weather conditions in the UK

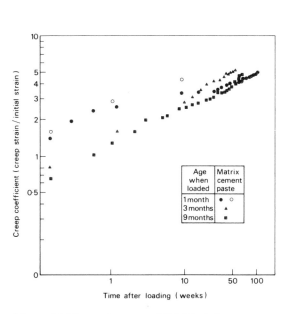

Figure 19 Flexural creep of GRC in indoor conditions

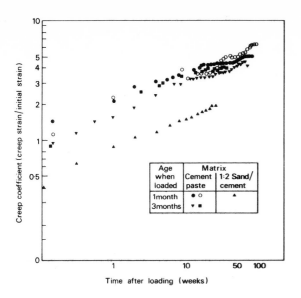

Figure 20 Flexural creep of GRC in water

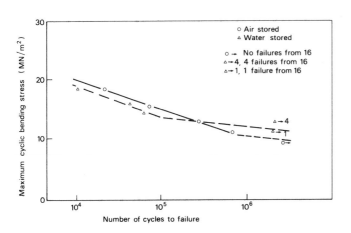

Figure 21 Flexural fatigue of GRC in air and water

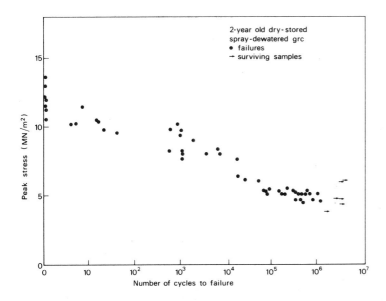

Figure 22 Tensile fatigue of GRC in air

55

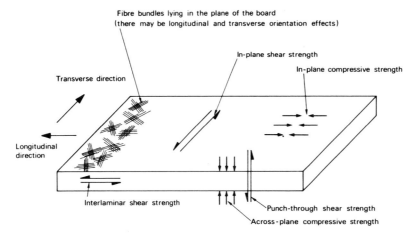

Figure 23 Anisotropy and directions in GRC

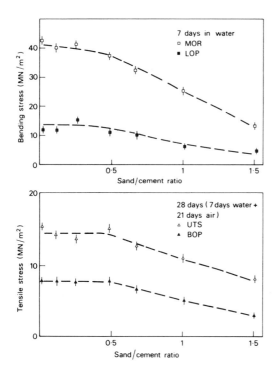

Figure 24 Effect of sand additions on MOR, LOP, UTS and BOP

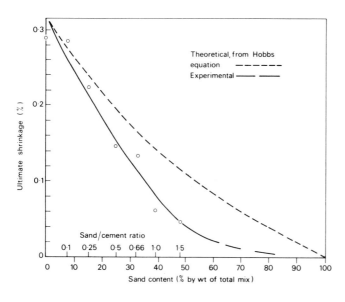

Figure 25 Ultimate shrinkage at 50°C against sand content for spray-dewatered GRC

Flexural fatigue of glass fibre reinforced cement (CP 12/76)

A.P. Hibbert and F.J. Grimer

INTRODUCTION

In recent years considerable interest has been shown in the reinforcement of gypsum plaster and Portland cement with small amounts of glass fibre for use in partitions, cladding panels, ducting, etc[1]. The latter material, grc, requires the use of alkali-resistant glass (Cem-FIL*) because of the high pH of hydrating cement which causes rapid degradation of the E-glass fibres used extensively in reinforced plastics[2]. Considerable work has been done on the static behaviour of this material, both in tension and bending, and some cyclic tensile tests have been reported[3]. The present paper, however, is concerned mainly with the effect of fluctuating stress on grc-type composites made in the form of large sheets (at the Building Research Station) by a spray-suction technique[4].

The behaviour of the material will be dictated by the characteristics of the matrix, the fibre and the fibre-matrix bond. All these will vary, to a greater or lesser extent, with time and the conditions under which the material is cured and stored. Results are therefore presented for a range of materials which had been stored under different conditions for various lengths of time.

EXPERIMENTAL METHOD

The results of fatigue tests on nominally identical specimens of any material show a large amount of scatter. With a material such as grc, the ultimate strength of which has a coefficient of variation of approximately 10 per cent, if any meaningful fatigue data are to be obtained a large number of specimens must be tested at each stress level. To achieve this a multiple specimen fatigue rig was developed which was capable of testing up to 16 specimens simultaneously in four-point bending (Figure 1). The load was applied to the rig by a hydraulically driven servo-controlled ram fitted to a steel frame and connected to the rig body through a load cell. A pin-jointed framework attached to the base of the frame divided the load equally between the 16 specimen positions. The loading and support bars were fitted with sleeves running on needle roller bearings to ensure that there was no resistance to flexure of the samples. The loading bars were free to move vertically in recessed channels the bottoms of which were fitted with rubber inserts to minimise the possible transference of shock loads to the rig when a specimen failed completely. The control equipment ensured that the desired load profile was maintained throughout the test, independent of the amplitude of ram travel, and hence regardless of any changes in the stiffness of the material. Microswitches were positioned at the bottoms of the loading bar channels and complete failure of the specimen resulted in their activation by the loading bar. Each microswitch was connected to a digital clock which recorded the time to failure of the specimen. Unless otherwise stated all the tests were carried out at a frequency of 3 Hz with the stress varying from zero to a predetermined maximum. In practice it proved necessary to maintain a small load at the minimum of the load cycle but this was so small as to have negligible effect on the results. In all cases the specimen dimensions were 150 x 50 x 10 mm.

The lives of the individual test pieces in each run were ranked in ascending order of magnitude and a probability of failure, P, assigned to each. This is best given by $i/(n+1)$, where i is the i th position in the ranked list and n is the number of specimens tested in the run (usually 16). The distribution of fatigue lives was assumed to be log-normal since analysis[5] of a sample of 32 failures at the same stress level had shown this to be a reasonable approximation. Using log-probability paper a straight line was drawn by eye through the data points to give a graph of number of cycles to failure (n) against P. The lines were not fitted by least squares analysis since this is not strictly applicable[6]. A typical probability v number of cycles line for grc is

---

* Registered trade mark of Pilkington Brothers Ltd

Figure 1 Multiple specimen fatigue rig

shown in Figure 2. It will be noticed that the points are not scattered randomly about the line as in a normal 'best straight line' but clustered in groups. This clustering is quite typical of this type of plot[6] and arises from the constraint that $n_{i+1} \geq n_i$ for all values of i.

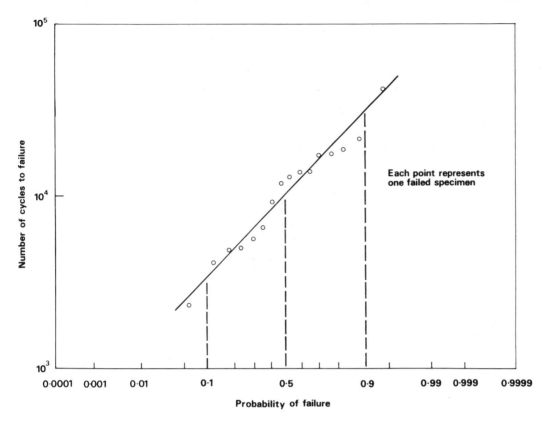

Figure 2 Typical probability v number of cycles line for grc

A series of runs at different maximum cyclic stresses then enabled the complete probability-stress-number of cycles to failure (PSN) field to be determined.

With the number of specimens tested at each stress level this method gives a very good estimate of the median life but, as with all fatigue investigations, it was difficult to obtain accurate values for the life at the 'tails' of the distribution. Though the median life was reproducible to within a few per cent of the log-life, the $P = 0.1$ level showed much more variation especially at higher life times; this is a reflection of the inadequacy of the log-normal distribution at the extremes. For this reason comparisons have been drawn between the median lives, ie $P = 0.5$, although some $P = 0.1$ lines have been drawn to indicate the scatter of life times that was observed in the material tested.

Since the input load to the rig was divided equally, each specimen was subjected to a slightly different stress because of small differences in thickness, an unavoidable consequence of the sheet fabrication processes. The coefficient of variation in stress for a run of 16 specimens was typically 6 per cent but there was no significant correlation between stress in an individual specimen and its position in the ranked list for the run. One of the main factors contributing to the scatter was local variation in glass content; this is discussed below.

MATERIALS

Glass fibre reinforced cement sheets made by the spray-suction process contain a nominal 5 per cent, by weight, of fibre incorporated in the form of chopped strands of approximately 204 filaments, of 9 μm diameter, each coated with a thin layer of pva or similar material. The strands are distributed evenly throughout the depth of the board and at random on its plane; their length can be varied from about 10 to 40 mm. The introduction of 5 per cent of fibres in this form imparts a certain amount of pseudo-ductility resulting in a high impact resistance for the material. The matrix may be modified by the addition of pulverised fuel ash (pfa), 40 per cent in this work, which provides a less aggressive environment for the fibres; or by the addition of certain polymers which enable a lower water:cement ratio to be used during the spray process and which also have a beneficial effect on the mechanical properties of the matrix.

After 7 days' storage under wet sacking, the sprayed boards, 1 m x 4 m x 10 mm, were cut into coupons approximately 150 x 50 x 10 mm. These were then randomised using a table of random numbers, and stored under the conditions described in Table 1 which also gives details of the composition and properties of the boards tested. The modulus of rupture and limit of proportionality (the latter may for practical purposes be regarded as the elastic limit or stress at first crack) were determined from slow bend tests on an Instron testing machine using the same four-point bending configuration as in the fatigue tests. At least six specimens were tested to obtain the values quoted.

In addition to the grc boards, some tests were also performed on an asbestos cement sheet typical of the type available commercially. Although these were of a limited nature they do allow some comparisons to be drawn between the fatigue behaviour of the two types of material.

RESULTS

The median lifetime stress v number of cycles curves for three grc boards and the asbestos cement sheet are given in Figures 3 and 4. When projected back to one half cycle the lines are in reasonable agreement with the statically determined modulus of rupture values at the time of test, although these values were obtained at a much slower rate of loading than that applied in the fatigue tests. At a loading rate equivalent to that of the fatigue tests the modulus of rupture may be substantially higher than that reported here. However, fatigue of concrete has been shown to be independent of frequency, and hence stress rate, from 4 to 20 Hz although the modulus of rupture may be up to 50 per cent greater than the static value at loading rates equivalent to that applied in cycling at 4 Hz[7].

When cycled with a maximum stress equal to that at the limit of proportionality, the grc boards had similar median lives, ie in the region 10^5 to 10^6 cycles (Figure 5).

There is little difference in the fatigue behaviour of specimens whether stored and tested in water after the initial 7–day curing period, or in air (Figure 6). The better fatigue life at the lower stress of those stored in water is due to an increase in the limit of proportionality resulting from a greater degree of cement hydration. Water-stored coupons were sealed in polythene bags with a little water before testing to ensure that they remained completely saturated, but it was found that allowing them to dry had negligible effect on the fatigue life and on the static ultimate strengths. Dry-stored specimens when saturated in water for several weeks before testing, showed a slight decrease in both static strength and number of cycles to failure but this was not significant compared with the performance of the asbestos cement sheet used in these tests, which showed a large change in both of these properties with absorbed water (Figure 4). The fatigue of asbestos cement was also time–dependent rather than cycle-dependent, in the region 1 to 3 Hz (Figure 7); an effect which was not observed with grc. If this time–dependence is a real property of asbestos cement and is not confined to the particular board tested here, then it is interesting to note that conventional fatigue testing may considerably over–estimate the lifetime of a component if it is subjected to only a slow cycling rate. However, the results obtained are of a very limited nature and further work is necessary to confirm this.

The effect of a change in fibre length from 10 mm to 40 mm was found to be negligible in an ordinary Portland cement/pfa matrix (Figure 8). This was not unexpected since the critical fibre length for such a composite is probably less than 10 mm.

Natural weathering over a period of 1 year resulted in a reduction in the gradient of the probability v number of cycles line consistent with the fall in modulus of rupture. There was little difference, however, in the fatigue limit at 10^6 cycles (Figure 9). The effect of over-stressing the material by applying a single cycle with a very high peak stress and then cycling to failure at a much lower level is shown in Figure 6.

The results of some modulus of rupture tests on specimens which did not fail during the fatigue tests are given in Table 2. The first group, board 7, shows that the residual strength of specimens cycled with a peak stress approximately equal to that at the limit of proportionality had dropped to about two-thirds of the original value after 10^6 cycles. This is very reasonable considering the large amount of internal damage on a microscale these specimens (which had only a small probability of sustaining this number of cycles) must have undergone. The second group, board 1, were subjected to a maximum cyclic stress about half that at the limit of proportionality and no specimens in the group of 16 failed within 10^6 cycles. The mean modulus of rupture of these does not differ significantly from the initial value, indicating that very little damage had occurred.

The mode of failure followed the conventional pattern for fatigue of materials in that the maximum

Table 1 Conditions of storage, composition and properties of the boards tested

Board	Matrix	Fibre length (mm)	Storage condition	Age at fatigue test (months)	At 28 days				At time of test			
					Mean MOR (MN m^{-2})	Coefficient of variation (%)	Mean LOP (MN m^{-2})	Coefficient of variation (%)	Mean MOR (MN m^{-2})	Coefficient of variation (%)	Mean LOP (MN m^{-2})	Coefficient of variation (%)
1	OPC	34	Water	3	-	-	-	-	42.0	5.7	13.2	9.9
2	OPC/40% pfa	22	Water	3	-	-	-	-	23.0	7.0	8.9	13.5
3	OPC	22	Water	9	-	-	-	-	22.0	20.0	11.6	14.0
4	OPC/40% pfa	10	Water	9	19.2	5.8	-	-	21.9	6.9	11.3	6.9
	OPC/40% pfa	43	Water	9	23.0	3.7	9.13	9.4	24.0	6.9	10.7	8.5
5	OPC	32	Natural weathering	12	35.4	10.5	-	-	22.0	9.2	-	-
6	OPC/40% pfa	42	Natural weathering	12	35.6	6.1	-	-	29.7	5.2	-	-
7	OPC	32	Air	6	39.4	5.0	11.3	6.9	37.0	4.0	10.2	9.9
	OPC	32	Water	6	32.4	6.8	15.9	3.4	27.9	7.4	16.7	1.9
8	Asbestos cement	-	Water	-	-	-	-	-	28.3	2.9	-	-
	Asbestos cement	-	Air	-	-	-	-	-	37.8	7.7	-	-

OPC = ordinary Portland cement; pfa = pulverised fuel ash; MOR = modulus of rupture; LOP = limit of proportionality

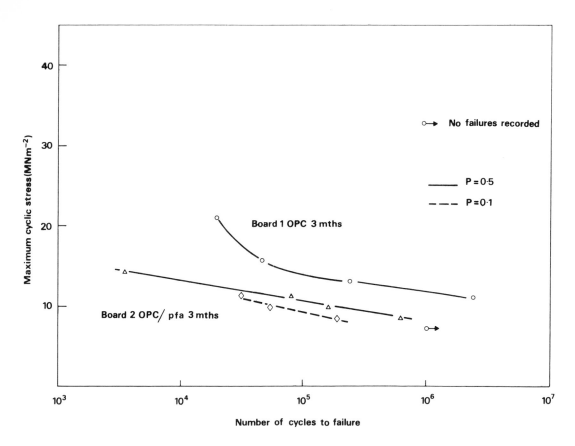

Figure 3 Probability-stress-number of cycles to failure

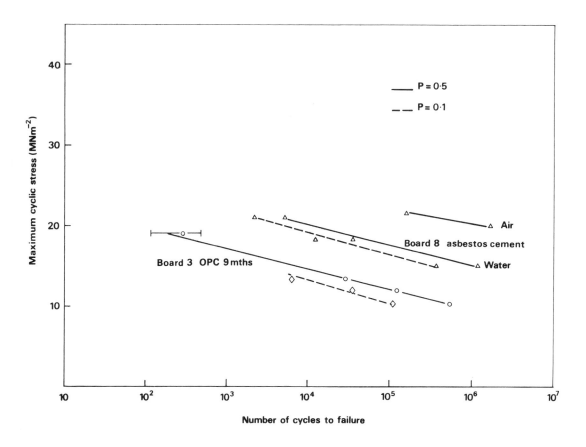

Figure 4 Probability-stress-number of cycles to failure lines for asbestos cement and grc boards

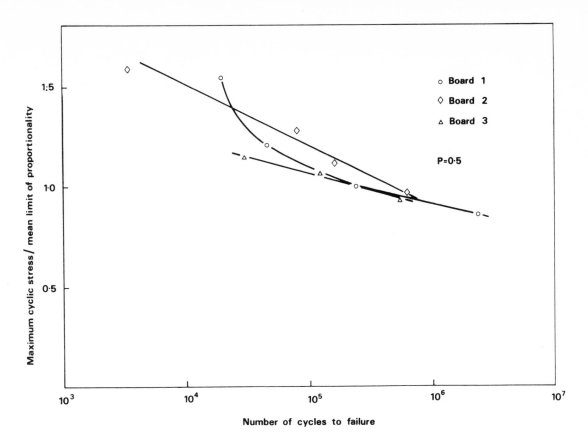

Figure 5 Number of cycles to failure

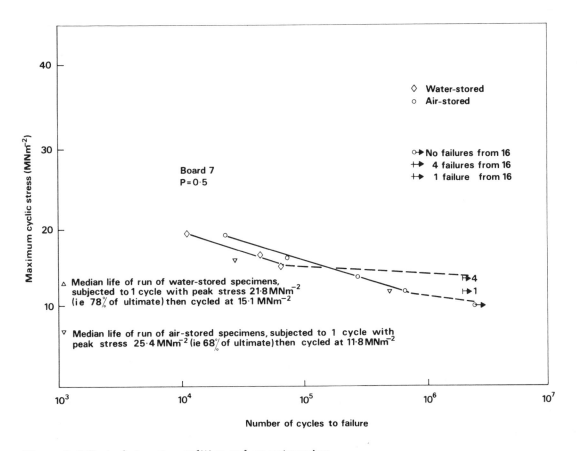

Figure 6 Effect of storage condition and overstressing

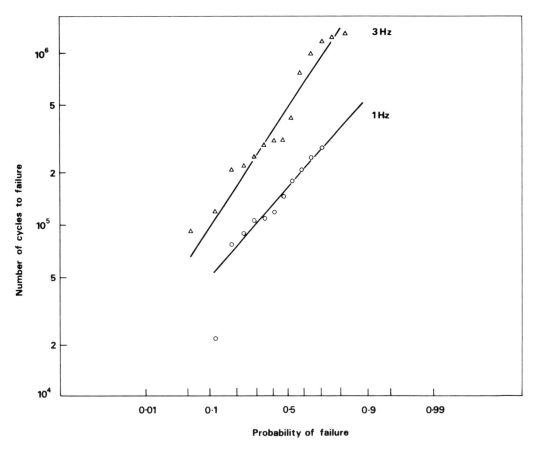

Figure 7 Effect of frequency on asbestos cement (mean maximum stress 21 MNm^{-2})

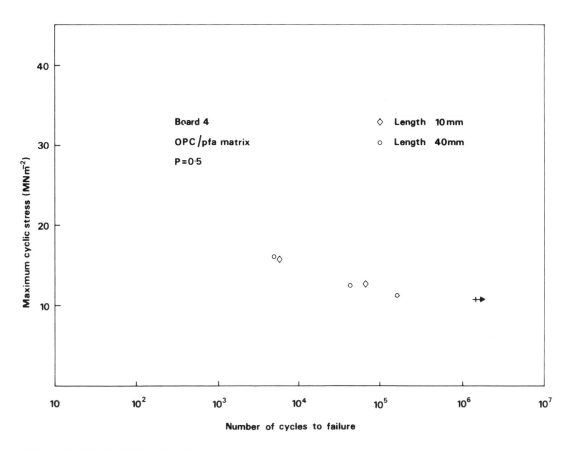

Figure 8 Effect of fibre length

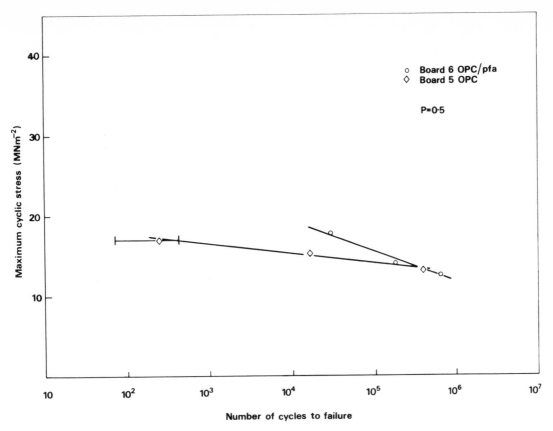

Figure 9 Effect of natural weathering over 1 year on boards with a matrix of ordinary Portland cement (OPC) and pulverised fuel ash (pfa)

deflection after the first few cycles remained constant during the major part of the test, ie up to about 90 per cent of the total number of cycles to failure. There was then a rapid rise and one or more cracks became clearly visible on the tensile face perpendicular to the direction of stress. The specimen then failed completely by the propagation of a single crack.

The amount of fibre pull-out varied quite considerably, being greater in the ordinary Portland cement/pfa boards at early ages than in the older ordinary Portland cement boards. This is consistent with the static behaviour where the material tends to lose some of its ductility as the bond between the fibre and matrix increases with age.

Using a method developed by one author[8] it was possible to make an assessment of the quantity of 'effective' reinforcement, ie that closely aligned to the direction of stress, in failed test coupons.

Forty-eight random specimens from the same board were tested in three groups of 16. Each was subjected to the same maximum cyclic load and the 1st, 2nd, 8th, 9th, 15th and 16th specimens to fail in each of the three runs were chosen for examination. This gave three groups of six representing early, median and late failures. Sections of equal depth, approximately 7 mm, were cut parallel to the crack as indicated in Figure 10, and were photographed by transmitted light. The number of strands in the tensile and compressive zones were counted assuming the

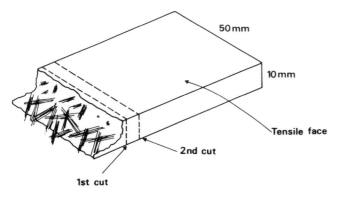

Figure 10 Diagram of failed specimen showing position of section

Table 2 Results of some modulus of rupture tests on specimens which did not fail during fatigue tests

Board	Maximum cyclic stress ($MN\,m^{-2}$)	Median life (cycles)*	No of cycles completed (n)	Probability of failure by n cycles*	MOR after n cycles ($MN\,m^{-2}$)	Mean initial MOR ($MN\,m^{-2}$)	Per cent of static strength remaining
Board 7, Air-stored LOP = $10.2\ MN\,m^{-2}$	11.7	6.0×10^5	1.3×10^6	0.98	20.4	34.3	59
	11.7	6.0×10^5	1.3×10^6	0.98	22.7	34.3	66
	13.5	2.5×10^5	7.8×10^6	0.82	19.8	34.3	58
	13.5	2.5×10^5	7.8×10^6	0.82	25.0	34.3	73
	13.5	2.5×10^5	7.8×10^6	0.82	21.6	34.3	63
Board 1, Water-stored LOP = $13.2\ MN\,m^{-2}$	7.3	–	1.0×10^6	No failures in run of 16 specimens	42.4[†]	42.0	100

* Taken from **P** : **n** line
† Mean of 6 specimens

LOP = limit of proportionality; MOR = modulus of rupture

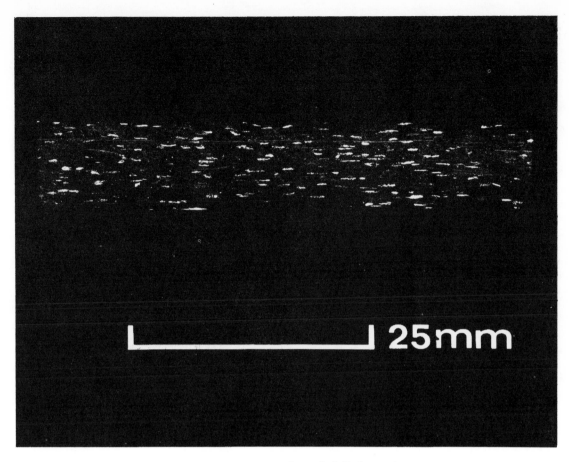

Figure 11 Photograph of representative section through failed specimen

Table 3 Number of strands in tensile and compressive zones of failed specimens

No of cycles to failure (x 10^4)	Total no of strands visible	No in compression region	No in tensile region
4.4	99	68	31
7.3	105	73	32
3.7	141	90	51
6.8	108	71	37
7.3	97	62	35
17.0	96	67	29
	Mean 108	Mean 71	Mean 36
12.3	123	81	42
12.9	118	70	48
14.3	103	61	42
15.3	109	67	42
13.9	125	73	52
16.0	110	65	45
	Mean 115	Mean 70	Mean 45
Greater than 50 x 10^4	119	68	51
	150	88	62
	117	70	47
	131	80	51
	129	78	51
	120	57	63
	Mean 128	Mean 74	Mean 54

neutral axis to be at half the specimen depth. Figure 11 shows a photograph of a representative section. From Table 3 it will be seen that coupons with a low lifetime were those which had a deficiency of reinforcement in the tensile region, ie the fatigue life for a given stress increases as the fibre volume fraction increases.

DISCUSSIONS AND CONCLUSIONS

It has been shown that the high cycle fatigue life of grc composites is closely related to the stress at first crack and is therefore controlled by the properties of the matrix rather than the fibre since until the matrix has cracked the stress carried by the fibre is small. Above the limit of proportionality the fatigue life is reasonably well represented by a straight line projected back to the static ultimate strength. Fatigue at these levels will be governed by the properties of the reinforcement and its bond with the matrix, failure taking place by a combination of fibre pull-out and breakage.

It has not been possible in the present work to determine whether an endurance limit as such exists for the material. This would require testing to be extended up to at least 10^8 cycles which would necessitate the use of cycling rates beyond the capability of the present equipment. There are strong indications, however, that the slope of the stress v number of cycles curve is reduced when the maximum stress is less than that at the limit of proportionality (Figures 3 and 6). At such low stresses it was found that very few, if any, specimens failed by 10^6 cycles which suggests a very high median life - in the order of 10^{10} cycles - especially since the scatter of results was observed to increase as the stress was reduced.

The results obtained for grc are consistent with those that have been reported for the repeated flexure of steel fibre reinforced concrete[9] where cycling at 90 per cent of the first-crack strength gave a fatigue life of 2×10^6 cycles with 2 to 3 per cent of fibre by volume.

ACKNOWLEDGEMENTS

The authors wish to thank Dr A J Majumdar for the help and encouragement he has given throughout this work and Mr A C Irwin who assisted with much of the testing.

REFERENCES

1 **Steele, B R.** Glass fibre reinforced cement. Proceedings of International Building Exhibition Conference, London, 1971.

2 **Grimer, F J** and **Majumdar, M A.** The strengths of cements reinforced with glass fibres. Magazine of Concrete Research, Vol 21, No 66, 1969, pp 23-30.

3 **Allen, H G.** Stiffness and strengths of two glass-fiber reinforced cement laminates. Journal of Composite Materials, Vol 5, 1971, pp 194-207.

4 **Ali, M A** and **Grimer, F J.** Mechanical properties of glass fibre reinforced gypsum. Journal of Materials Science, Vol 4, No 5, 1969, pp 389-395.

5 **British Standards Institution.** BS 3518 : Part 5 : 1966. Methods of fatigue testing - Guide to the application of statistics.

6 **Hahn, G J** and **Shapiro, S S.** Statistical models in engineering. John Wiley and Sons, 1968, Chapter 8.

7 **Galloway, J W** and **Raithby, K D.** Effects of rate of loading on flexural strength and fatigue performance of concrete. Transport and Road Research Laboratory TRRL Report LR 547, 1973.

8 **Hibbert, A P.** A method for assessing the quantity and distribution of glass fibre in an opaque matrix. Journal of Materials Science, Vol 9, No 3, 1974, pp 512-514.

9 **ACI Committee 544.** State-of-the-art report on fiber reinforced concrete. Journal of the American Concrete Institute, November 1973, No 11, Proceedings Vol 70, pp 729-744.

Properties of glass fibre cement – the effect of fibre length and content (CP 94/75)

M.A. Ali, A.J. Majumdar and B. Singh

The properties of glass fibre reinforced cement composites (grc) containing alkali–resistant fibres of lengths 10–40 mm and volume fractions 2–8 per cent have been studied. At 28 days the optimum properties of the composite were achieved, with 6 volume per cent fibre addition. These were four to five times the bending strength, three to four times the tensile strength and 15 to 20 times the impact strength of the unreinforced cement paste. Further increase in the fibre content increases the porosity of the composite resulting in the lowering of bending and tensile strengths. The stress and strain of the composite at matrix cracking increased with increasing fibre contents. No significant improvements in the modulus of the composite were observed over the range of fibre additions investigated. The trends in the properties of grc as affected by the variations in volume fraction and length of the fibre, and environmental conditions of curing of the composites, are qualitatively related to the degree of cement hydration, changes in porosity of the composites and fibre/matrix interfacial effects. The change of properties of grc with time (strengths tend to decrease), and long-term studies are in progress.

1. Introduction

The mechanical properties of a fibre composite depend very strongly on the proportion of the fibre used and its dimensions. Most of the work on glass fibre cement (grc) reported from this laboratory [1] has been carried out with composites containing 4 vol% of 34 mm long cem-FIL† alkali-resistant glass fibres arranged in an approximately two-dimensional random array. The main objective so far has been the establishment of long-term properties of such a composite. Considerable progress has been made in, this direction [2] and it has now become necessary to optimize the properties of grc composites for specific uses. A study was, therefore, undertaken aimed at assessing the effect of fibre content and fibre length on grc properties. The present paper describes the 28-day results, and as the properties of grc change with time (strengths tend to decrease), long-term studies are in progress.

2. Materials

A batch of ordinary Portland cement (OPC) was selected for the entire programme of work. The physical and chemical properties of this cement are listed in Table I.

The glass fibre was supplied by its manufacturer in the form of rovings having 30 strands or ends, each containing 204 individual filaments of 10 to 12 μm in diameter. The fibres were sized following the usual commercial practice.

3. Fabrication

Composite boards measuring 1.5 m × 1 m and approximately 10 mm thick were produced by the mechanised spray-suction method described

elsewhere [3]. It is important to point out that this method of fabrication produces a random two-dimensional distribution of short fibres in the plane of the boards. Fibre lengths chosen for the present investigation were 10, 20, 30 and 40 mm

TABLE I Physical and chemical properties of ordinary Portland cement used

(a) Physical properties

Water for standard consistency	25.3%
Setting time	(a) initial 2 h 10 min
	(b) final 3 h 30 min
Fineness	332 m^2 kg^{-1}
Soundness	2 mm expansion
Compressive strength of vibrated mortar cubes in N mm^{-2} at:	
24 h	14
3 days	35
7 days	50
28 days	66

(b) Chemical composition

Oxide	wt %
SiO$_2$	21.6
Fe$_2$O$_3$	1.84
TiO$_2$	0.31
P$_2$O$_5$	0.35
Mn$_2$O$_3$	0.15
Al$_2$O$_3$	4.30
CaO	65.28
MgO	1.18
Na$_2$O	0.15
K$_2$O	0.42
SO$_3$	3.06
Loss on ignition	1.04
Free lime	1.94

† Trade mark of Pilkington Brothers Ltd.

respectively and these were easily obtained by adjusting the number of blades in the cutting roller of the glass chopper.

The fibre contents of grc boards were calculated from the quantities of cement, glass and water used in the fabrication and the weight of the demoulded board. These calculations were checked by weighing the quantities of glass fibre obtained by washing small areas of a green demoulded board. The calculated and measured glass contents agreed reasonably well (differences of the order of 5 to 10% were sometimes noticed).

During the fabrication, grc boards with different fibre contents and lengths, offered different resistance to the de-watering process. To achieve a reasonably constant water/cement ratio in the demoulded boards, the duration of suction and the amount of water extracted had to be controlled. Even then the final water/cement ratio of the boards in the series varies between 0.26 and 0.32.

4. Curing

24 h after demoulding, the 150 mm × 1 m strips were sprayed with water, covered with a polythene sheet and stored in the laboratory for six days. During this period the strips were sawn to give 150 mm × 50 mm test specimens. All test specimens, therefore, underwent a regime of wet curing lasting for 7 days. They were subsequently cured either in water at 18° C or in air of 40% r.h. also at 18° C. The test specimens were assigned randomly to the alternative curing conditions and pre-selected test ages to ensure that the systematic variations in the fabrication of the sheets were not confounded with the effects of the variables under investigation. The long axis of all test specimens coincided with the long axis of the board, this being the direction in which the spray-head moves in discrete steps.

5. Testing

The density of the composites was computed from the measured values of the weight and volume of the 150 mm × 50 mm test coupons which were stored in air for 21 days following the inital 7 day wet-curing.

Tensile and four-point bend tests were carried out on a Universal Instron testing machine following the procedures described previously [4]. An extensometer of 50 mm gauge length was clamped directly on the tensile test specimen for the measurement of strain. Two separate specimens were used to measure strain values corresponding to both faces and an average value was taken for constructing stress—strain diagrams. The impact strength was measured using an Izod tester of 12 J capacity.

In grc composites prepared by the spray-suction method, the location of the glass "layer" near the surface is very rarely the same for both faces. Consequently, a systematic variation in bending strengths is often observed depending on which face of the specimen is subjected to tension. Of the six specimens routinely tested in bending three were placed on the machine with their top face (as fabricated) up, the other three with top face down. The average of all six values was taken as the bending strength of the composite.

6. Results

The experimental results of the present study are plotted in Figs. 1 to 5 and 7 to 11. Fig. 6 shows two idealized tensile stress—strain graphs, corresponding to two typical grc composites. The figures are generally self-explanatory and illustrate the effect of varying the length and concentrations of glass fibre reinforcements on some of the properties of grc composites, kept in two different environments. The coefficients of variation in strength measurements of six specimens were in

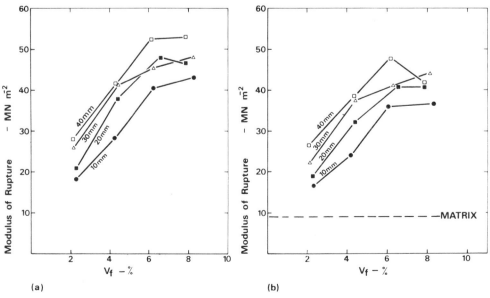

Figure 1 Relation between fibre volume fraction and modulus of rupture of grc at 28 days for different fibre lengths. (a) Stored in air, (b) stored in water.

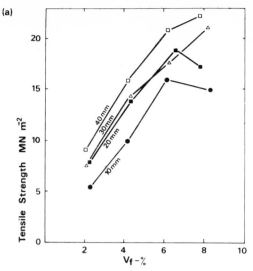
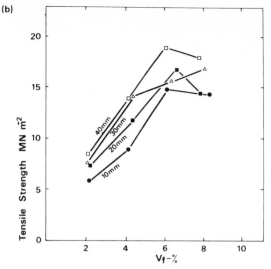

Figure 2 Relation between fibre volume fraction and tensile strength of grc at 28 days for different fibre lengths. (a) Stored in air, (b) stored in water.

the range 9 to 11% for bending and tensile and 15 to 20% for impact strength.

In Figs. 5, 9 and 10, either the stress or the strain at the limit of proportionality (LOP) have been plotted against fibre volume percentages. The LOPs may be defined as the points where the load—deflection curve in bending or the stress—strain curve in tension deviates from linearity and they signify the termination of the elastic regime in the life of the composite under increasing load (see Fig. 6). These points are not always easy to determine by visual examination of the graphs. A reasonable accuracy is called for, however, in locating the LOP since in many instances it may mark the commencement of the cracking of the composite.

In Fig. 10 the experimental values of the matrix cracking strain have been plotted against fibre volume percentages for both air- and water-cured grc composites. According to the recent theory developed by Aveston *et al.* [5—7] for brittle-matrix composites, an increase in the failure strain of cement is to be expected from the addition of glass fibres. The basic relationships of the theory [5] need a slight modification before they can be applied to grc as described here, to take into account the specific geometry of glass fibre strands. These reinforcements usually have a rectangular cross-section assuming the form of a tape in larger lengths. The modified expression for matrix cracking strain ϵ_{mc}:

$$\epsilon_{mc} = \left[\frac{6 P \tau \gamma_m E_f (\eta V_f)^2}{E_c E_m^2 A_f V_m} \right]^{\frac{1}{3}}$$

has been used to predict the increase in the failure strain of the matrix. The values of the various parameters used in the calculations are given in Table II. The factor η refers to the orientation efficiency factor. Calculations depicted in Fig. 10 were carried out with three values of η, $2/\pi$, $\frac{1}{2}$ and $\frac{3}{8}$ since it is not definite yet as to which particular value is the most appropriate for the composites studied.

TABLE II Parameters used in the calculation of matrix failure strain

Symbol	Definition	Value assumed in the calculations
τ	Fibre—cement interfacial bond strength	$3\,\mathrm{MN\,m^{-2}}$
γ_m	Surface work of fracture of matrix	$10\,\mathrm{J\,m^{-2}}$
E_m	Young's modulus of cement paste	$26\,\mathrm{GN\,m^{-2}}$
E_c	Young's modulus of the composite	$30\,\mathrm{GN\,m^{-2}}$
E_f	Young's modulus of fibre	$76\,\mathrm{GN\,m^{-2}}$
V_f	Fibre volume fraction	
A_f	Effective area of the glass fibre strand	$0.027\,\mathrm{mm^2}$
P	Perimeter of glass fibre strand	$1.42\,\mathrm{mm}$
η	Orientation efficiency factor	

7. Discussion of results
7.1. Strength
It is evident from Fig. 1 that for all fibre lengths used, the modulus of rupture of the composite (calculated assuming elastic behaviour) increased with increasing fibre proportions. The rate of increase in strength is quite rapid initially, extending up to about 6 vol % of fibre addition beyond which more fibres seem to have little effect. In some cases a decrease in MOR beyond 6 vol % fibre concentration has been observed. In general air-stored specimens gave slightly higher MOR values than those of the corresponding water-stored ones.

These effects of fibre additions are mirrored in the tensile strength results illustrated in Fig. 2. Again, there is an indication that for most fibre lengths, strength values reached their maxima in both environments when the fibre concentration was about 6 vol %. There is also evidence to suggest that tensile strength increases, as in the case of MOR, with increasing fibre length. This arises because the length efficiency factor for reinforcement is higher for longer fibres.

The rule of mixtures predicts that composite strengths should vary linearly with fibre volume percentages and indeed this is nearly the case in Fig. 1 and 2 up to a limiting fibre percentage of 6 vol %. Beyond this point, the porosity of the composite increases rapidly. This is clearly manifest in Fig. 3 where the density of the composite has been plotted against its fibre content. In any

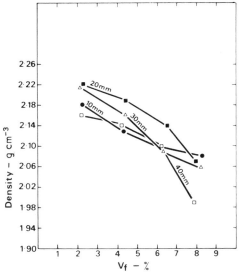

Figure 3 Relation between fibre volume fraction and density of grc composites at 28 days for different fibre lengths.

large-scale manufacturing method as has been used here it is well nigh impossible to ensure that all fabrication variables are kept under strictest control. In the manufacture of grc composites such variables are many, notably the distribution of the fibre, penetration of the fibre bundle by the matrix and the compaction of the composite. Some of the nonsystematic variations in the properties of the composite as affected by changes in fibre lengths and contents illustrated in Fig. 1 and 2 can be accounted for by the difficulties in producing fibre composites of uniform density from a particulate matrix. For such a composite

there has to be an upper limit of fibre addition beyond which the reinforcing action of the fibre cannot be effectively utilized. For grc prepared by the spray-suction method, this limit seems to be in the neighbourhood of 6 vol % fibre in the composite. There is also some indication that the optimum length of fibres to be used in these composites is less than 40 mm. In considering the effect of fabrication variables on the porosity of the composite it has also to be borne in mind that glass fibre strands comprising 204 individual filaments have a built-in porosity and its contribution to the total porosity of the composite is obviously dependent on both fibre content and fibre length as well as the integrity of the roving.

At the optimum level of fibre addition namely 6 vol %, the MOR values of the grc composites at 28 days were 4 to 5 times better than that of the unreinforced matrix. The corresponding improvement in tensile strength was 3 to 4 times.

The impact strength of grc composites (Fig. 4) increased with increasing fibre contents up to the limit of fibre additions (~ 8 vol %) employed in this study, in both air and water environment. The increase in the porosity of the composite resulting from fibre additions is an advantage here since it allows a reduction in the interfacial bond strength. A greater proportion of the fibre thus becomes available for pullout which, in the main, controls the work of fracture or impact strength of brittle matrix composites. The 28-day impact strength of grc having 6 vol % glass fibre is 15 to 20 times better than that of the unreinforced matrix. The impact strength seems to increase with increased fibre length, again on account of "pull-out" considerations.

In common with tensile and bending strength results, the impact strength of grc was higher in air storage than in water storage. When cured in water, cement hydrates to a greater extent than in air, the products of hydration filling the voids in the matrix as well as in the fibre strands. The over-

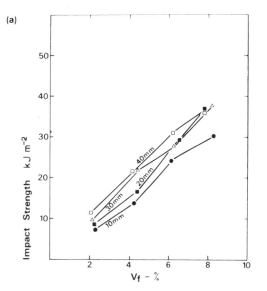 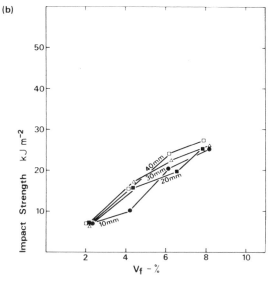

Figure 4 Relation between fibre volume fraction and impact strength of grc at 28 days. (a) Stored in air, (b) stored in water.

all porosity of the composite is thus reduced relative to air storage. The strands may, therefore, become less flexible, losing some of the inter-filamentary friction. The impact strength of the composite is likely to decrease under these conditions.

In the air storage, the corrosive action of the cement on glass fibres is much less pronounced thereby allowing the reinforcement to retain a larger proportion of its pristine tensile strength. The strands being more flexible in air storage have a better chance of aligning themselves in the direction of stress during pull-out or elastic extensions after the multiple cracking of the matrix. Shrinkage of the cement may also produce a stronger frictional component of the interfacial bond. These factors combine to produce a high strength efficiency factor for the reinforcement and consequently the MOR and tensile strength of the composite are higher in air than in water. Obviously some of these factors will have a deleterious effect on the impact strength of the composite. With present knowledge it is not possible to treat this matter in a quantitative way.

It has already been reported [2] that the strength of grc changes with time and in certain environments a decrease in strength has been noted. The effect of fibre content and fibre length on these changes in grc properties is under investigation.

7.2. Stress—strain

It is seen in Fig. 5 that the stress at the LOP in bending also reaches a maximum value around 6 vol% fibre concentration in both air and water environments. The explanation based on porosity variations advanced in the previous section applies here also. Since the composite behaves elastically up to the LOP and the fibres are strained only a

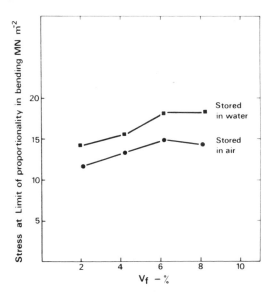

Figure 5 Relation between limit of proportionality (LOP) in bending and fibre volume fraction of grc composites at 28 days.

little because of the very low failure strain of the matrix. the contribution of the matrix to the LOP

stress is the predominant factor here. Cement, when cured in water, develops a higher strength relative to air curing. This is reflected in the higher LOP stress in bending given by grc composites kept immersed in water. At 6 vol% fibre addition the stress at the LOP in bending of 28-day old composites were 30 to 50% higher than that of the unreinforced matrix.

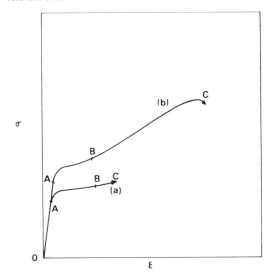

Figure 6 Idealized stress—strain curves of grc at 28 days. (a) Low fibre content of short lengths; (b) high fibre content of long lengths.

The experimental stress—strain curves in tension obtained with grc composites having various proportions of 30 mm long fibres are presented in Fig. 7. and Fig. 8 shows similar curves for 4 vol% fibre composites containing fibres of various lengths. Both sets of curves also show the effect of curing conditions. In Fig. 6 two idealized stress—strain curves have been drawn for two typical combinations of fibre length and fibre content. These curves consist of three distinct regions — a linear elastic region OA terminating at the LOP where the fibre and the matrix undergo similar deformations, a region of multiple cracking of the matrix AB as described by Aveston *et al.* [5] and a final portion BC where the stress in the composite is supported by the elastic extension and pull-out of the fibres. It will be appreciated that the point on the stress—strain curve at which multiple cracking commences is almost impossible to locate as the curve bends over after the LOP.

It is seen from Fig. 7 that the increase in the stresses and strains at the LOP caused by the increase in fibre concentrations is higher in the case of water-stored samples. As mentioned before this is due to the matrix developing greater strength in water. When the proportion of the fibre in the composite is low, the stress at which multiple cracking of the matrix takes place remains constant. At higher fibre contents this stress shows an increasing trend suggesting a progressive transfer of stress across the interface. The measured strain values at the end of the "multiple cracking" regime showed a considerable scatter and it was not possible to judge its depend-

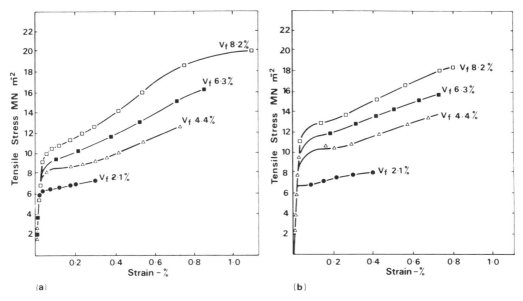

Figure 7 Tensile stress–strain curves of grc composites containing 30 mm long fibres with different fibre volume fractions at 28 days. (a) Stored in air, (b) stored in water.

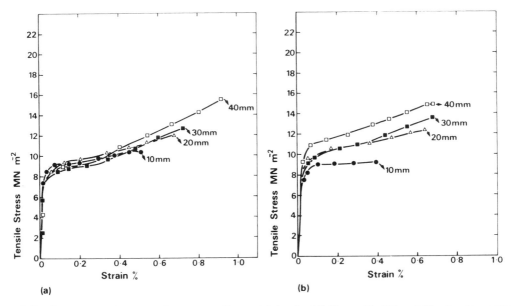

Figure 8 Tensile stress–strain curves of grc composites containing 4 vol % fibres with different fibre lengths at 28 days. (a) Stored in air, (b) stored in water.

ence on fibre concentrations. The slope of the third region showed an increase, as is to be expected, with increase in fibre volume percentages. The ultimate failure strain of the composite when stored in air increased from 0.3% at 2 vol% fibre addition to 1.2% at 8 vol% fibre addition.

The ultimate failure stress and strain of the composite were slightly higher in the case of grc specimens cured in air. This point has been discussed in the previous section.

The variations in fibre lengths do not influence the tensile stress–strain behaviour of grc composites nearly to the same extent as changes in the fibre content (Figs. 7 and 8). The greatest benefit brought about by the increase in fibre lengths is seen to be the improvement in the ultimate failure stress and strain of the composite.

The effects of fibre content on the cracking stress and strain of the matrix are plotted separately in Figs. 9 and 10. It has been assumed

for this exercise that the cracking of the matrix begins at the LOP when the composite specimens are subjected to tension.

It is evident that the presence of fibres delays the onset of matrix cracking in proportion to the fibre content. As the properties of the cement matrix are strongly dependent on curing conditions, it is only logical to expect that the initial cracking of the composite will also be subject to the same variations. The cracking strain of the composite specimens is lower in air than water storage (Fig. 10), due to the shrinkage of the matrix. For air stored specimens, therefore, the measured cracking strain has to be corrected for shrinkage [5] in order to arrive at the true matrix cracking strain for comparison with theoretical predictions. In so far as there is positive evidence that the cracking strain of the matrix increases with fibre content, the present study supports the theory put forward by Aveston *et al.* [5–7]. How-

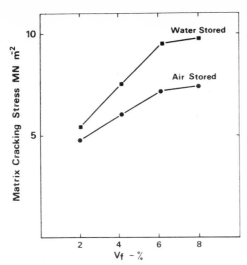

Figure 9 Relation between matrix cracking stress and fibre volume fractions for grc composites at 28 days.

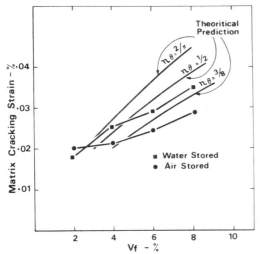

Figure 10 Relation between matrix cracking strain and fibre volume fraction for grc composites at 28 days.

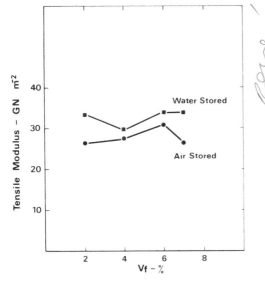

Figure 11 Relation between fibre content and tensile modulus for grc at 28 days.

ever, for a random two-dimensional composite such as grc as described here, the use of the efficiency factor of $2/\pi$ or $\frac{1}{2}$ predicts a larger effect than is obtained experimentally at high glass content (Fig. 10). A factor of $\frac{3}{8}$ suggested by other

workers [8, 9] brings the predicted values nearer to those reported here. A further point to consider is whether accurate theoretical predictions are possible in the present case where the composites do not have uniform porosity and variations in porosity are known to affect the properties of cement pastes markedly.

The initial modulus of grc composites containing different fibre percentages as determined from their respective tensile stress–strain curves are shown in Fig. 11. Since the fibre/matrix modular ratio is only 3 to 4 for grc, large changes in the modulus of the composite are not expected from the rule of mixtures when the fibre content is changed from 2 to 8 vol %. The modulus is marginally higher in water-stored samples because they are denser due to the fact that cement hydrates to a greater extent in water than in air. When the modulus of the matrix was calculated from the composite modulus values given in Fig. 11 by using the rule of mixtures, sometimes a value larger than the measured value of the modulus of cement paste having a water to cement ratio of 0.3 was obtained. It cannot be ruled out that some of the free water was concentrated in or near the fibre bundle thereby reducing the amount of water available for cement hydration. The modulus of the matrix phase would increase under this condition.

8. Conclusions

(1) Although glass fibre concentrations of up to 10 vol % can be incorporated in a cement matrix by the spray-suction method, many of the 28-day properties of the resulting composite, notably its bending and tensile strength at the limit of proportionality and at failure attain their maximum values at 6 vol % fibre addition. These properties also show an increase with increasing fibre lengths, the rate of increase being most pronounced in the 10 to 30 mm range.

(2) The 28-day impact strength of grc composites increases with increasing fibre length and fibre content up to the limits investigated.

(3) At 28 days, grc composites containing 6 vol % of 30 mm long fibres gave 4 to 5 times the bending strength, 3 to 4 times the tensile strength and 15 to 20 times the impact strength of that of the unreinforced matrix. The failure stress and strain of the cement matrix are also considerably improved.

(4) At 28 days grc composites are slightly stronger in air than in water. However, their modulus of elasticity and stresses at the limit of proportionately are higher in water.

(5) The trends in grc properties as affected by variations in the concentration or length of the fibre and curing conditions are qualitatively relatable to (a) changes in the porosity and compaction of the composite (b) degree of cement hydration and (c) interfacial effects.

(6) It must be remembered that only 28-day

values of various properties of grc are given in this paper. Longer term studies are in progress; some of these show a decrease in strength properties and all results will be reported in due course.

Acknowledgements

The work reported here was carried out in collaboration with Pilkington Bros Ltd. The work described has been carried out as part of the research programme of the Building Research Establishment of the Department of the Environment and this paper is published by permission of the Director, and of H.M.S.O., holders of Crown Copyright.

References

1. B. R. STEELE, "Prospects for fibre reinforced construction materials", Conference proceeding of International Building Exhibition. (Building Research Station, London, 1971) BRS Current Paper No. CP 17/72.

2. A. J. MAJUMDAR and R. W. NURSE, *Mater. Sci. Eng.* **15** (1974) 107.

3. F. J. GRIMER and M. A. ALI, *Mag. Concr. Res.* **21** (66) (1969) 23.

4. M. A. ALI and F. J. GRIMER, *J. Mater. Sci.* **4** (1969) 389.

5. J. AVESTON, G. A. COOPER and A. KELLY, "The properties of fibre composites", Paper 1, Conference proceedings National Physical Laboratory (IPC, 1971) p. 15.

6. J. AVESTON and A. KELLY, *J. Mater. Sci.* **8** (1973) 352.

7. J. AVESTON, R. A. MERCER and J. M. SILLWOOD, "Composites – standard testing and design", Conference proceedings National Physical Laboratory 8/9 April 1974 (IPC, 1974) p. 93.

8. V. LAWS, *J. Phys. D: Appl. Phys.* **5** (1971) 1737.

9. H. KRENCHEL, "Fibre reinforcement" (Akademisk forlag, Copenhagen, 1964).

Glass fibre reinforced cement (CP 79/74)

A.J. Majumdar and R.W. Nurse

SUMMARY

Glass fibre reinforced cement is introduced as a new composite material, based on a matrix of cement or cement and fine filler reinforced with a relatively small addition of strands of alkali-resistant glass. The glass content is relatively low, being restricted by increasing difficulty of mixing and compacting as the glass content is increased. For any method of mixing and placing and varying with the mix proportions there is an optimum value of glass content in relation to bending strength; impact strength rises steadily with glass content. When premixing an additive is required, commonly polyethylene oxide or methylcellulose. Premixed formulations can be placed by tamping and vibration, pumping or extrusion. An effective method is to mix and place simultaneously by spraying the matrix as a slurry into a stream of chopped glass fibre from a spray chopper. The combined sprays are directed on to a suction mould where excess water is removed. Properties of composites prepared by the various methods are compared. The impact strength and fire resistance of glass fibre reinforced cement are particularly good. Examples of practical applications are given.

1. INTRODUCTION

Cement and concrete products are notable for their weakness in tension unless reinforced by steel rods, and for their lack of toughness which gives rise to frequent cracking under impact loads, thermal shock or dimensional changes due to humidity variation. The use of fibres to overcome such deficiencies is traditional in building, animal, vegetable and asbestos fibres all being used in various sheet materials. The possibility of using glass fibre to reinforce cement or concrete by making use of the high tensile strength, moderate Young's modulus and high fibre lengths obtainable has long been recognised. Early attempts to use glass in this way were not very successful, and it soon became known that alkali derived from the cement was bringing about deterioration of the types of glass then available.

One way of using glass is to make up ropes of glass rovings joined together and coated with plastics so as to make a reinforcing bar or cable directly replacing steel reinforcement [1]. The thick coatings used in making up these also protect them from attack by the cement. Experiments have been carried out with unstressed reinforcement and with stressed reinforcement. The modulus of the glass is rather low for the former method to be efficient, but the combination of low modulus with high tensile strength makes stressed reinforcement a promising field [2,3]. For this application too heavy a coating of resin is a disadvantage, as it leads to long-term creep in the bond between cable and concrete. Although resin coated glass reinforcements show some distinct advantages, for instance under load, smaller cracks are generated and they are more uniformly distributed, the reinforcements are too expensive in comparison with steel for them to be of interest except in special circumstances, e.g., when cover is so thin that steel bars would suffer atmospheric corrosion. Such applications will not be considered further in this review, which deals with a different technique, that of mixing glass fibres with cement, mortar or concrete. Pioneering work was done in this field by Biryukovich and co-workers [4] who used various low-alkali cements, or cement with polymer, in conjunction with a borosilicate glass. The glass was in various forms, including woven mats, and glass contents of up to 50% by weight of the finished product were achieved. Advantages claimed were high tensile strength, high degree of elasticity in thin sections, watertightness and good thermal, acoustic and dielectric properties. Some prototype structures, such as thin shell roofs, were constructed.

Currently available borosilicate glass fibres

are not suitable for reinforcing a matrix based on ordinary Portland cement on account of their poor performance in an alkaline medium. In collaboration with the Building Research Station, Pilkington Brothers Limited have recently developed a new range of alkali-resistant glass fibres generically described as Cem-FIL* which promises to obviate the difficulties met with other glass fibres. Cement-based composites made by using this fibre are undergoing extensive trials in several laboratories in the United Kingdom.

Very little has been reported on the use of glass fibre to reinforce concrete in mixes containing coarse aggregate greater than 5 mm. In early investigations in this area the issue was clouded by the unknown incidence of attack by cement on the glass fibres. Results obtained with the alkali-resistant glass fibre, Cem-FIL, showed that the most important advantage to be gained by reinforcement of concrete with such fibres is an increase in its long-term impact resistance. Thus the work to failure as measured by the area under the load/deformation curve to the point of failure is increased 4–5 times by an addition of about 3% of fibre by weight of the finished concrete. The effect is noticeable with additions of fibre as low as 0.5%. In general however the addition of fibre to a concrete mix at constant water/cement ratio leads to such a decrease in workability that the mix cannot be compacted fully by ordinary means. Thus any advantage in static strength obtained from the fibres is compensated and eventually lost because of increased porosity and this happens at quite low glass contents. Using hand compaction or vibration to place the concrete and a non-filamentising type of fibre there is an increase in bending strength up to a fibre content of about 3%. Compressive strength and splitting tensile strength show a general fall for all fibre additions.

Although more work is needed on the use of glass fibre in concrete, the probable advantages to be gained could only be economical under special circumstances. Glass reinforced cement is much more promising and will form the main subject of this review. By glass reinforced cement is meant a composite material produced by using glass fibre and a paste of neat cement or cement plus fine aggregate. This may be considered to be a new composite material, resembling to some extent asbestos cement. Glass reinforced gypsum plaster is another new material; it closely resembles glass reinforced cement and may be used as a model to study some aspects of such fibrous composites where ageing and chemical effects require elimination.

* Registered trade-mark of Pilkington Brothers Limited.

2. MATERIALS

2.1. Glass

The only form of glass commercially available in the form of single filaments is wool. The best alkali-resistant glasses will not form wool easily and wool is in any case extremely difficult to mix with cement or plaster. Nevertheless, because of its relative cheapness, an interest in glass wool for reinforcement of cement is maintained.

The more usual form of glass fibre is the roving. In the manufacture of glass fibres each filament is drawn from a platinum tip covering a hole in the bottom of a heated platinum tank or bushing. The bushing has a large number of holes, commonly 204 or 408, and the glass is collected on a rotating drum or collet as a strand of that number of filaments. Before winding the strand passes through an applicator which coats the glass with a size. The cake of glass fibre so formed is dried and several cakes are then rewound together to form a roving; if necessary the original strand is split into a number of strands. The glass manufacturer is able to control the 'integrity' of the roving; that is the ease with which it breaks up into its constituent strands without also breaking up the strands into filaments. The fibre is marketed as a 'cheese' of roving which may be unwound from the inside and fed to a chopping machine to produce any convenient length. Alternatively the glass may be obtained from the maker as chopped strands, or as chopped strand mat. Mat consists of glass strands chopped to a suitable length (commonly a mixture of 50 mm and 25 mm). The strands are laid randomly on a conveyor and a binder is employed to hold them together as a mat.

When it is desired to concentrate the glass fibre reinforcement into a particular plane, and to take advantage of directional reinforcement, crenette may be employed. This is a mesh of strands cemented together at points

TABLE 1

Chemical composition of some glasses available as fibre (weight per cent)

	E-glass	A-glass	Alkali-resistant glass
SiO_2	52.4	72.2	71
K_2O) Na_2O)	0.8	13.0	11
B_2O_3 ·	10.4	—	—
Al_2O_3	14.4	1.8	1
MgO	5.2	3.5	—
CaO	16.6	9.5	—
ZrO_2	—	—	16
Li_2O	—	—	1

of contact. The warp can be heavier than the weft or vice versa, and the number of crossing strands per unit length can be varied in the two directions. These types of fibre have commonly been available in E or A glass. Both compositions are readily attacked by contact with moist cement, and alkali-resistant glass which is attacked much more slowly by a cement matrix is now produced on a pilot scale. The approximate chemical compositions of the three glasses are given in Table 1. The properties of single filaments are given in Table 2.

The resistance to alkali attack of the glasses in fibre form has been measured both by the reduction in diameter [5] and the reduction in strength after standard immersion conditions [6]. Individual uncoated fibres were mounted on polyethylene frames, immersed in some selected solutions which were contained in polypropylene bottles and kept in constant temperature baths. The conditions used were: $N/1$ NaOH at 100°C for 1½ hours, saturated $Ca(OH)_2$ at 100°C for 4 hours, or 'cement

TABLE 2

Properties of single filaments of glass

	E-glass	A-glass	Alkali-resistant glass
Density (g/cm³)	2.54	2.46	2.78
Tensile strength (MN/m²)	3500	3100	2500
Modulus of elasticity (GN/m²)	72.5	65	70
Extension at break (%)	4.8	4.7	3.6

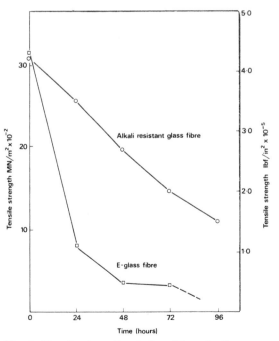

Fig. 1. Tensile strength of glass fibres in the aqueous solution phase of Portland cement at 80°C.

TABLE 3

Alkali resistance of glass fibres

Average reduction (per cent) in fibre diameter at 100°C

Glass	$N/1$ NaOH, 1.5 h	Saturated $Ca(OH)_2$, 4 h
Pyrex	22	2
E-glass	59	9
A-glass	15	10
Alkali-resistant glass	5	< 1

effluent' solution at 80°C. The composition of this solution at room temperature (NaOH 0.88 g/l, KOH 3.45 g/l, $Ca(OH)_2$ 0.48 g/l, pH = 12.5) was chosen to simulate the aqueous phase of a Portland cement slurry.

Results for reduction in fibre diameter are given in Table 3 and for reduction in tensile strength in Fig. 1.

2.2. Cements

The matrix of greatest interest is ordinary Portland cement (OPC) [7]. This consists of a mixture of cement clinker as it comes from the kiln, ground together with a few per cent of gypsum. The gypsum on hydration forms a complex calcium sulphoaluminate with lime and alumina released from the clinker. The hydration of calcium silicates accounts for most of the strength of the set cement; calcium hydroxide is released during hydration and very frequently crystallises in the pores, forming well-developed crystals of considerable size. The pH of the aqueous phase in equilibrium with set Portland cement is 12.5—13.0. Normally, the total of $Na_2O + K_2O$ in the unhydrated cement is 0.5—1.75%.

Reactive siliceous powders known as pozzolanas may be added to Portland cement and during setting these react with the calcium hydroxide released by the cement to form further quantities of hydrated calcium silicate. Consequently the pH and alkalinity of pozzolanic cement are lower than those of Portland cement alone. A frequently used pozzolana is pulverised fuel ash (pfa).

High alumina cement [8] differs from Portland in forming no calcium hydroxide on setting and in depending for its strength on hydrated calcium aluminates. The pH of aqueous phase in contact with the set cement is 11.8—12.05 and the cement is low in total alkalies (0.15—0.20%). Storage of the set cement under warm moist conditions brings about chemical changes which result in a considerable fall in strength; this effect is more marked the higher the water/cement ratio.

The compositions of the aqueous phases in contact with the set cements are given in Table 4. The cements or mixtures were added

TABLE 4
Composition of the aqueous phase in contact with various cements

g/litre	Portland cement	60% Cement 737 + 40% pfa	60% Cement 737 + 40% pozzolana	High-alumina cement
Ca	0.71	0.53	0.51	0.16
Na	0.24	0.33	0.28	0.06
K	0.57	0.56	0.54	0.30
Alkalinity as (OH)	1.04	0.95	0.87	0.67
pH	12.7	12.65	12.60	12.05

to water at a water/solids ratio of 5:1 and the suspension agitated by rolling for 18 days at 20°C. The pozzolana was a high quality natural pozzolana from Italy. The lower values for calcium concentration and alkalinity shown in columns 3, 4 and 5 indicate that these matrices will be less aggressive to glass than the Portland cement.

Portland and other hydraulic cements expand if allowed to set and harden while stored in water. On drying they undergo a shrinkage which is only in part reversible if the cement paste is subsequently re-wetted. These relationships are shown diagrammatically in Fig. 2. The expansion of neat cement paste in water depends a great deal on the composition of the cement, but is of the order of 0.3% change in length after immersion for a year. Irreversible drying shrinkage is from half to one-third of the total shrinkage, which may amount to 0.2—0.3% and increases with fineness of cement and water/cement ratio.

The porosity of fully compacted set Portland cement and therefore most of its mechanical properties depend on the water/cement ratio used in mixing and on the age of the cement paste. If the ratio is below about 0.4, unhydrated cement will remain indefinitely in the set paste. Portland cement paste consists of a porous gel, unhydrated cement, calcium hydroxide crystals and capillary pores. The pores of the gel are thin slits with an average width of 15—30 Å whereas the capillary spaces vary over a range with diameters of up to several hundred Ångstroms. Capillary porosity can be calculated from the evaporable water content, which is defined as the water lost on drying the saturated surface-dry paste over magnesium perchlorate at 23°C in vacuo.

The volume changes on drying and differences in porosity may both be expected to influence the adhesion between fibre and cement in a composite.

The setting of plaster is accompanied by an expansion and is due to the conversion of calcium sulphate hemihydrate to gypsum. In the same way that cement strength is lower for high water/cement ratios, the porosity and strength of set plaster depend on the water/plaster ratio. The α-hemihydrate, prepared by an autoclaving process, requires less water than the normal β-hemihydrate for the same workability. Since plaster is inert towards glass, composites of plaster and E glass give satisfactory performance indoors. Calcium sulphate is soluble in water, so such composites cannot be used outdoors unless protected. Because set plaster does not attack glass, it will be convenient to illustrate some of the properties of brittle matrix composites by reference to glass reinforced gypsum instead of cement.

3. SIMPLE THEORY OF FIBROUS COMPOSITES

In a composite with continuous fibres aligned parallel to the direction of the application of the load the Young's modulus of the composite E_c is given by the lower limit of the Voight estimate provided that the Poisson's ratios of fibre and matrix are identical

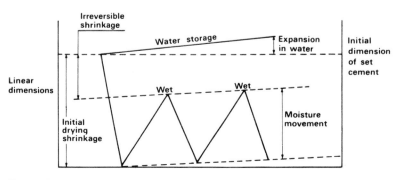

Fig. 2. Dimension changes during hardening of Portland cement.

TABLE 5

Properties of composite components

Property	Fibre	Plaster	Cement
E (MN/m^2)	7.6×10^4	1.7×10^4	1.7×10^4
σ (MN/m^2)	1210	2.75	2.75
τ (MN/m^2) in composite		5.52	10.34
l (mm) in composite		43	34
l_c (mm) in composite		22.2	11.8

[9]. The Poisson's ratio for glass fibre is 0.22 and for cement paste or gypsum plaster 0.20–0.30 depending on the water/solid ratio. Hence the relation

$$E_c = E_f V_f + E_m V_m$$

should be applicable. E and V are Young's modulus and volume fraction respectively and the subscripts c, f and m refer to composite, fibre and matrix. A similar relation applies to the ultimate tensile strength,

$$\sigma_c = \sigma_f V_f + \sigma'_m V_m,$$

where σ'_m is the stress supported by the matrix at composite failure.

For composites containing chopped fibres not aligned with the direction of loading it is necessary to introduce efficiency factors η_l for length and η_o for orientation.

$$\sigma_c = \eta_o \eta_l \sigma_f V_f + \sigma'_m V_m.$$

Krenchel [10] has shown by a statistical model that $\eta_l = 1 - l_c/l$ where l is the actual fibre length and $l_c/2$ is the length of fibre that will just support the breaking stress. If τ is the interfacial bond strength and d the fibre diameter then

$$\frac{l_c}{l} = \frac{\sigma_f d}{2\tau l}.$$

Krenchel also derives η_o for various typical situations; $\eta_0 = 1/5$ for fibres distributed randomly in a volume and 3/8 for fibres dis-

tributed randomly in a plane. Majumdar and Ryder [6] have made calculations for sprayed composites, for which the orientation factor 3/8 is appropriate. Tables 5 and 6 are taken from their work.

In this type of composite the reinforcing element is a fibre bundle of 204 filaments, not a single fibre. In the calculations it was assumed that τ for the bundle surface was that measured by pull-out tests on glass rods but the bundle perimeter was estimated assuming cylindrical packing with 25% voids. Majumdar and Ryder [6] explain the greater divergence between theory and experiment at the higher glass content by the inefficient wetting of the fibre and consequent poor compaction and low density which sets in as the glass content is raised.

In the simple analysis the bond strength is assumed to remain constant during pull-out. Various attempts [11,12] have been made to derive improved efficiency factors assuming an initial debonding followed by frictional pull-out. The main difficulty in assessing these theories is the experimental determination of the interfacial bond strength. For glass fibres this should preferably be determined using bundles with the same make-up and surface coating as those used in the composite. With a cement matrix the bond strength also depends strongly on the age of test and the conditions of curing. These effects have been demonstrated by pull-out tests on thick fibres by de Vekey and Majumdar [13,14].

TABLE 6

Properties of composites

Property	Grg		Grc
	6.8 wt.% glass	12.6 wt.% glass	4.3 wt.% glass
V_f	0.047	0.089	0.0325
E_c (MN/m^2)			
Calculated	1.77×10^4	1.83×10^4	1.76×10^4
Experimental	1.72×10^4	1.72×10^4	1.72×10^4
σ_c (MN/m^2)			
Calculated	15.40	29.65	12.10
Experimental	13.80	21.80	13.40

4. FABRICATION

The method used to fabricate a fibrous composite influences the final properties in two ways; it determines the maximum glass content that can be tolerated before decreasing density offsets any gain in reinforcement, and it determines the fibre orientation efficiency. For example, premixing gives a random three-dimensional array unless the mix is subsequently extruded or pressed; the spray-suction method gives a random two-dimensional arrangement. Filament winding gives a one-dimensional array or a multi-angled oriented array. Moulds and forming methods can usually be designed to take advantage of these properties.

4.1. Premixing

Mixing fibre with cement or cement and aggregate is facilitated by using an additive; polyethylene oxide 0.02—0.04% by weight of dry materials or methylcellulose 0.2—0.75% were found to be suitable [15]. Another factor influencing mixing behaviour is the type of fibre; a highly filamentising roving is very difficult to mix uniformly in contrast with a roving of high integrity. Finally, a pan type mixer is preferred. Without the additive, or with it, a drum mixer causes the fibre to segregate into balls or mats. This happens in whatever order the constituents are added. The best results are obtained by mixing the additive with about 80% of the mixing water in a bucket, adding the chopped glass fibre and stirring well and then pouring the mixture into a Cumflow-type or similar mixer. The other dry constituents are then added, mixing is begun and the rest of the water is added during mixing. The additive and the water form a gel which prevents the fibres from becoming matted and improves the workability and moulding properties of the mix. By these methods up to 7.5% of a filamentising roving (by weight of dry solids) can be mixed using an additive and the same limit applies to an integral roving either with or without additive.

Compaction is difficult especially for mixes of high fibre content. In hand fabrication moulds are filled in layers about 25 mm thick and tamped; finally the mould is vibrated with a Kango hammer. Alternative methods of placing premixed fibre reinforced cement include pressing, injection moulding and extrusion.

4.2. Pressing

Boards were made successfully in a 100 × 100 mm laboratory press, in a Fielding and Platt paving flag press and in a 1000 tonne press (panel size 1.4 × 0.8 m, 6—27 mm thick). It is necessary in the pressing process for the initial mix to be sufficiently fluid to flow readily into all parts of the mould, with a minimum of mechanical spreading and levelling. Sufficient water must be expelled during pressing to reduce the water/cement ratio to an acceptable level, to produce a product with sufficient green strength for immediate handling and to carry a proportion of fines to the filtered surface in order to produce a smooth well filled surface. The addition of fibrous material speeds up the filtration rate and allows the expulsion of a larger quantity of water. On the other hand, the thickening agent used in mixing reduces the rate of filtering. Good panels have been pressed from mixes incorporating either methylcellulose or polyethylene oxide thickening admixtures. The type and amount of admixture are critical, however, depending on the mix design and pressing conditions, *i.e.* pressure and pressing speed.

A typical successful mix with the paving flag press was equal parts by weight of ordinary Portland cement (OPC), zone 3 sand and pfa, initial water/cement ratio 0.8, 0.04% polyethylene oxide; content of 11 mm long glass fibre was 1.7% by weight of dry solids, pressing pressure 11 MN/m^2. On the 1000 tonne press the best mixes were OPC/pfa 1.5:1 and OPC/pfa/sand 1:1:1, incorporating 0.2% methylcellulose and 2.5% glass fibre 22 mm long; pressing pressure was 0.7 MN/m^2 and pressing speed 45 mm/min (considerably slower than the paving flag press). Initial water content was chosen for ease of filling and levelling in the moulds, which were provided with perforated plates for dewatering, covered with Fibreflex paper-felt filters. Final water content was determined by weighing the pressed slab.

4.3. Injection moulding

Generally pumps with valves are unsuitable for pumping glass fibre mixes because the fibre accumulates around the valves and causes them to jam. Good results have been achieved with peristaltic pumps, a Challenge Squeeze-crete and a Delasco LY5 OD both giving good service. A thickening admixture is required to stop the mix bleeding when subjected to pumping pressures. Vibration of the feed hopper was required with some mixes to ensure an even flow. Some of the components prepared by injection moulding are described in Section 6.

A problem with injection moulding is the inclusion of air which is then difficult to remove because of the presence of fibre. This results in a number of defects. Small regular blowholes of about 2 mm diameter at the cast surface can be reduced if the mould surface is absorbent. Larger irregular voids, both at the surface and internally, were reduced by fitting a vacuum box round a perforated section of the pipeline just before the inlet to the mould.

4.4. Extrusion

The first experiments on extrusion were carried out in a modified screw-type clay extruder. The 160 mm diameter barrel of this machine reduces to a rectangular outlet 76 mm × 55 mm and solid extrusions of these dimensions were made. The maximum pressure in the machine was about 0.1 MN/m². A range of OPC/pfa, OPC/sand and OPC mixes with varying amounts of fibre was tried, and it was found that a thickener was essential to prevent bleeding and blocking of the die. Various die shapes were then tried and extrusion was successful but at the water contents required shape retention after extrusion was poor, and could not be remedied by the use of calcium chloride or by heating the die. Addition of bentonite also failed to achieve its purpose. The best extrusion was an OPC/sand mix 1:1 with a w/c ratio of 0.45. The glass content was 2.5% of 22 mm fibre and 2% methylcellulose was added, both calculated as a weight per cent of the dry solids.

A ram type extruder capable of exerting higher pressures (max. 6.5 MN/m²) was constucted. It consisted of a 177 mm bore tube reducing to 102 mm at the die end, pressure being applied to the mix by a rubber piston actuated by a hydraulic ram. High pressures combined with a dry mix were required for satisfactory extrusion with a larger than usual dosage of thickening agent. Water/solids ratios were 0.25—0.35 and methylcellulose was added up to 0.75% by weight of dry solids.

The main problems were: bleeding, which could be reduced by increasing the quantity of thickener, and air entrainment, which led to explosive expansion on leaving the die. This latter problem would probably be overcome by application of vacuum to the mix before reaching the die. In further development of extrusion attention is required to die design, mix design and the arrangement for taking away the product. However, successful extrusions up to 5 m long of a channel section 100 × 55 × 12 mm thick were achieved using an OPC/sand mix with 2.5% of 22 mm long fibre and 0.75% methylcellulose. Limestone sand gave especially good results.

4.5. Spray—suction technique

Cement slurry of water/cement ratio 0.5—0.6 was prepared and poured through a sieve into the hopper of a pump spray unit. A glass-chopper was mounted with the spray gun and these were arranged so as to allow the stream

Fig. 3. Production of boards by the spray—suction method.

of chopped fibres to meet the spray half-way between the spray gun and the mould. Rovings of glass were fed to the chopper and fibre strands of the required length were sprayed together with cement slurry on to the paper covered perforated metal face of a suction mould. The mould had adjustable screed boards round its edges to allow sheets of various thickness to be made [16]. Figure 3 shows a mechanised version of the equipment, developed to produce uniform boards up to 4 m × 1 m in size. The material was sprayed evenly over the mould face until the required thickness was obtained. The top surface was then levelled off with a straight edge and the excess water was extracted at a suction of 70—80 kN/m² over about 5 minutes. The mould was then reversed and used as a suction pad to carry the sheet to a pallet for demoulding. Different lengths of fibre (10—50 mm) could be obtained by varying the number of blades in the chopper. The glass/binder ratio was controlled by the number of rovings fed to the chopper.

The green sheet so obtained can be remoulded, provided that the bends are not too sharply radiused. In this way corrugated or folded sheets, pipes, ducts and tubes are made. Decorative surfaces can be provided by trowelling coloured fine aggregate into the surface.

Because of its versatility, the uniformity of the products and the advantage of the random orientation of the fibres in two dimensions, the spray suction method is preferred for some product forms in comparison with other mixing and forming processes.

5. PROPERTIES

The properties of the composites were mea-

TABLE 7

Properties of E-glass

Diameter of fibre filament	8—10 micrometres
No. of filaments in a strand	204
Fibre tensile strength	2.4 GN/m^2
Modulus of elasticity	7.25 × 10^{4}MN/m^2
Coating on fibres	Polyvinyl acetate

TABLE 8

Properties of gypsum plasters

	Plaster of Paris	α-Hemi-hydrate
SO$_3$, %	38.6	39.0
CaO, %	52.5	52.7
Loss on ignition at 290°C, %	6.3	6.1
Transverse strength MN/m^2 (BS 1191-1967)	7.2	12.1

sured on specimens sawn from boards 8—10 mm thick. Direct tensile strength was determined on 25 mm × 150 mm samples in an Instron machine at a crosshead speed of 2.0 mm/min. For flexural strength specimens 50 mm × 150 mm were tested in four point loading over a span of 135 mm equally divided into three parts. For impact testing two machines were used; an Izod tester taking specimens 25 mm × 150 mm and a Charpy taking specimens 50 mm × 70 mm, the conversion Izod × 0.92 = Charpy being used to normalise the results when necessary. For all three tests the width and thickness were measured over the failure section.

5.1. Effect of glass fibre content

The effect of glass fibre content on physical properties will first be illustrated by reference to plaster reinforced with E glass, fabricated by the spray—suction method and by premixing. The properties of the E glass are given in Table 7 and of the two plasters used in Table 8. The α-hemihydrate contained a retarder; 0.1% keratin was added to the plaster of Paris. Sheets after demoulding were dried for 72 hours in laboratory air before being sawn into test specimens. These were then stored at 40% R.H. and 18°C until tested.

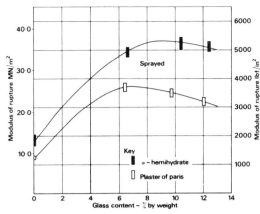

Fig. 4. Modulus of rupture and glass content of glass reinforced gypsum.

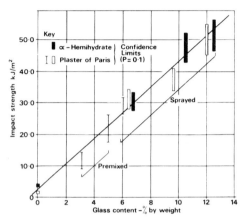

Fig. 5. Impact strength and glass content of glass reinforced gypsum.

Figure 4 shows the relation between modulus of rupture and glass content (50 mm fibre length) for composites made from the two types of plaster. Composites made with the α-hemihydrate were stronger because this plaster retains less water and therefore gives a higher density. Both plasters show an optimum addition of fibre after which the increasing difficulty of compaction more than offsets the increased reinforcing effect. A similar plot for impact strength is shown in Fig. 5. In this case there is no optimum, the relationship being essentially linear.

Table 9 gives data for glass reinforced cement made by the spray—suction process. For the modulus of rupture, the substantial increase up to 7.5 wt.% of glass fibre levels off between 7.5 and 10.0%. Impact strength appears to increase linearly with increasing glass content. These results are in substantial agreement with those given earlier for glass fibre reinforced gypsum.

In Fig. 6 the modulus of rupture and density are shown for three mixes prepared by the premix method and compacted by tamping and vibration. In this case an optimum glass content of 2.5% by weight of the dry solids is indicated for the OPC mix, but for the sand mortar or fly ash mortar strength is still rising at 5% of glass.

TABLE 9

Modulus of rupture and impact strength of composites for varying glass content and varying glass length

Glass content (wt. %)	Glass length (mm)	7 days storage		28 days storage			
				In air		In water	
		MOR (MN/m²)	IS (kJ/m²)	MOR (MN/m²)	IS (kJ/m²)	MOR (MN/m²)	IS (kJ/m²)
2.5	10	16	6	18	8	17	7
	20	20	9	21	9	19	7
	30	23	7	24	10	22	6
	40	25	9	28	12	27	7
5.0	10	24	13	28	14	24	10
	20	32	18	38	17	32	16
	30	39	17	41	22	38	17
	40	40	22	42	22	38	15
7.5	10	31	20	—	—	—	—
	20	41	24	49	29	41	20
	30	38	23	46	28	41	22
	40	44	25	53	31	48	24
10.0	10	34	32	43	30	37	28
	20	32	30	46	47	33	25
	30	48	26	57	38	44	27
	40	43	30	53	35	42	27

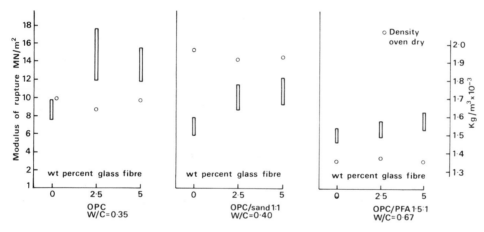

Fig. 6. Modulus of rupture, density and glass content for 3 mixes.

Taking all the results together it can be seen that the optimum glass content for modulus of rupture depends on the type of mix and the method of fabrication, the final falling off being caused by a decrease in workability. Impact behaviour is governed by the pull-out of fibre and is not adversely affected by a fall in density such as is experienced over the range of glass contents tested.

5.2. Effect of glass length

Each of the glass contents listed in Table 9 was tested at four different glass lengths up to a maximum of 40 mm. Modulus of rupture and impact strength both increased markedly up to 30 mm glass length, but changed very little between 30 and 40 mm. It seems likely that these properties are little changed by increasing the glass length beyond 40 mm.

5.3. Effect of method of manufacture

Table 10 gives modulus of rupture, impact strength and density for composites with a matrix of neat Portland cement, made up by four different processes. All boards were stored in laboratory air for two days, sawn to size and then cured at 18°C, 60% R.H. until tested at 28 days. The hand moulded and pressed mixes contained 0.2% of methylcellulose and the extruded mix 0.8%. In respect of bending strength spray suction and extrusion are superior. This is in part due to low water/cement ratio, but is largely to be attributed to the greater efficiency of reinforcement of the two-dimensional arrangement obtained with spray suction and the partial alignment in the direction of extrusion for the extruded product. Impact strength is insensitive to these factors and is better for the lower density

85

TABLE 10
Properties of composites made by four processes . Age at test: 28 days; 20 mm glass fibre: matrix neat Portland cement

Method of manufacture	Spray—suction	Hand-moulded premix	Extruded premix	Pressed premix
Modulus of rupture MN/m^2	21.2	9.8	18.0*	13.5
Impact strength (Charpy) kJ/m^2	8.1	8.6	9.0	9.2
Density (oven dry) kg/m$^3 \times 10^{-3}$	2.18	1.60	1.74	1.80
Glass fibre (wt. % of dry materials)	3.25	2.5	2.5	2.5
Water/cement ratio	0.30	0.40	0.26	0.10

* Tested // to the extrusion direction.

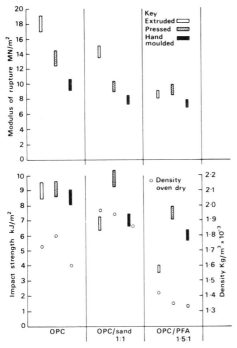

Fig. 7. Modulus of rupture, impact strength and density, 3 processes, 3 mixes. Glass content 2.5 wt.%, 22 mm long.

mixes when allowance is made for the higher glass content of the spray—suction boards.

In Fig. 7 further comparisons are made between the three premix processes for OPC, OPC/sand and OPC/pfa mixes. The relatively coarse sand is a better filler than pfa for mixes that are to be extruded.

5.4. Products made by spray—suction

Unless specified otherwise it may be assumed that the composites contain 4.0—5.0 vol.% of alkali-resistant glass fibre and that the water/cement ratio in the finished board is approximately 0.30.

Typical stress—strain curves in tension are shown in Fig. 8 for two ages and two storage conditions. More detailed curves have been obtained by Allen [17] using an extensometer. The curves consist of two parts: a linear elastic portion which terminates when the matrix cracks and a quasi-plastic region which extends up to ultimate failure. The tensile cracking strain of neat-cement paste varies with water/cement ratio and age over

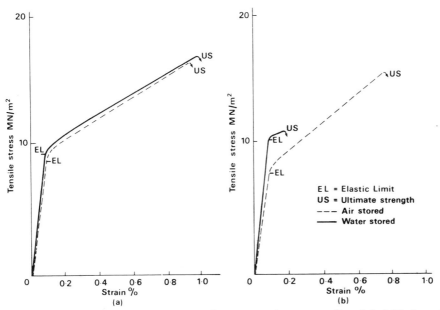

Fig. 8. Stress—strain curves in tension of spray—suction composites; (a) at 28 days, (b) at one year.

TABLE 11

TABLE 11

Properties of composites made by spray-suction, glass content 5% of 34 mm fibres (28 days air storage)

Modulus of elasticity GN/m^2	20—22
Tensile strength MN/m^2	15—18
Bending strength (modulus of rupture) MN/m^2	36—40
Impact strength (Izod) kJ/m^2	22—25
Density g/cm^3	2.0—2.1
Drying shrinkage %	0.32—0.35
Moisture expansion %	0.10—0.15
Thermal expansion mm/mm per deg C	10.6 × 10^{-6}

the range of 0.02—0.08% as compared with a strain at the elastic limit in the composite of 0.06—0.10%. It may be concluded on this and other evidence that the toughness of the matrix is little affected by the relatively small amount of fibre used in these composites. Prolonged storage under saturated conditions changes the nature of the stress strain curve nearer to that of a brittle material; this effect is supported by other evidence (*e.g.* impact testing) and is discussed further later.

The properties of the composite material after 28 days air storage (18°C, 60% R.H.) are given in Table 11.

5.5. Effect of prolonged storage on mechanical properties

Specimens 150 mm × 25 mm × 10 mm were cut in a randomised pattern from boards 4 m × 1 m × 10 mm, stored either in air at 18°C and 40% R.H. or continuously under water at 18°C. The glass content was 5% by weight of the finished board in the form of

fibres 34 mm long. Up to sixty specimens were tested for each of the mean values shown in the graphs of Fig. 9. Statistical analysis of one set showed that the 90% confidence limits were ± 7% of the mean for the modulus of rupture measurements and ± 14% of impact strength; these limits were assumed to be valid for the whole series. A brief description of these results has been given recently by Steele [18]. Figure 9 shows modulus of rupture against log time for composites made with alkali-resistant glass in air and in water; the results for E-glass were so similar for the two storage conditions that they have been grouped together. Corresponding impact strengths are given in Fig. 10. Figure 11 gives modulus of rupture results for alkali-resistant glass in air and water storage for a matrix of Portland cement + 40% pfa; results on E-glass are for water storage only. The corresponding impact strengths are given in Fig. 12. The initial rise in strength of the alkali-resistant glass composites can be attributed to an improvement in the bond between matrix and fibre. After 28 days the strength of air stored composites falls gently but after 3 years still exceeds the 7-day value. The E-glass composites fall steadily in strength, especially in impact strength, over the whole period of the test. Composites made from alkali-resistant glass and stored continuously in water show a more pronounced fall in strength than those stored in air. A linear relation between strength and log time has been assumed in Fig. 9 because this kind of relationship was also found in accelerated tests at higher temperatures. However, it could equally well be concluded that there is an arrest in the decline in strength between 1 and 3 years. The long term fall in strength can be explained by a decrease in the glass fibre strength, but it is not clear whether this is due to residual alkali

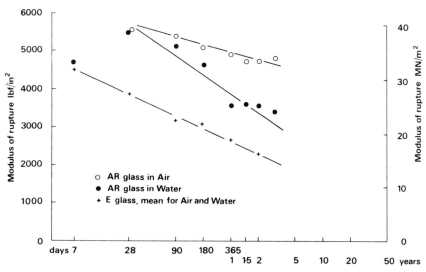

Fig. 9. Modulus of rupture against log time for composites made with E glass or alkali-resistant glass. Air and water storage.

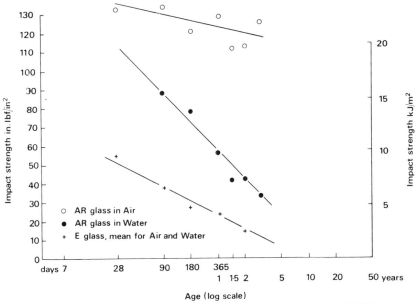

Fig. 10. Impact-strength against log time for composites made with E glass or alkali-resistant glass. Air and water storage.

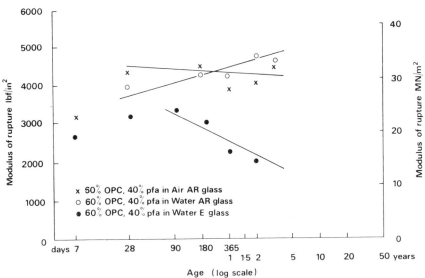

Fig. 11. Modulus of rupture against log time for alkali-resistant glass and E glass in OPC + 40% pfa. Air and water storage.

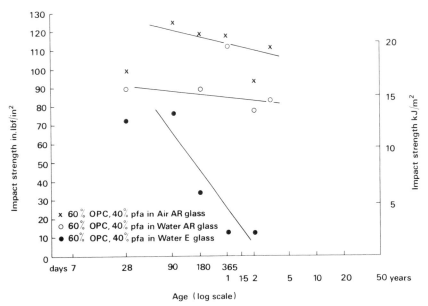

Fig. 12. Impact strength against log time for alkali-resistant glass and E glass in OPC + 40% pfa. Air and water storage.

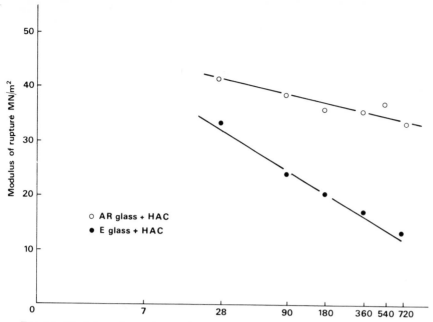

Fig. 13. Modulus of rupture against log time for E glass or alkali-resistant glass with high alumina cement matrix. Water stored.

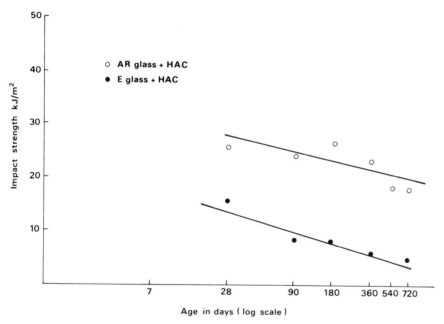

Fig. 14. Impact strength against log time for E glass or alkali-resistant glass with high alumina cement matrix. Water stored.

attack or mechanical damage to the fibre caused by crystal growth in the cement matrix. Those composites with a cement/pfa matrix, which crystallises less calcium hydroxide during ageing, show a continuous rise in strength, although the initial value is lower than that of a composite with a cement only matrix. At ages longer than a year the cement/pfa composites are stronger than the cement only composites.

Impact strength is more strongly reduced by ageing than is bending strength and this is confirmed by the change in the nature of the stress—strain curve (Subsection 5.4). The effect is probably a combination of fibre weakening and changes in the interfacial condi-

tions, leading to fibre fracture rather than pull-out.

Both these factors can be controlled by the application of a suitable coating material on glass fibre strands and/or the modification of the matrix. The impact strength of cement/pfa composites stored under water (Fig. 12) is substantially better than those of composites prepared from the unmodified cement (Fig. 10). The addition of water-durable polymer emulsions to the cement matrix or the use of suitable fibre coatings should also be helpful in improving the fracture-toughness of GRC. Some of these aspects are the subject of continuing research.

Results obtained with E-glass and high

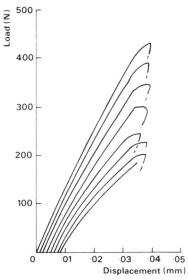

Fig. 15. Typical load/beam displacement result. Matrix only.

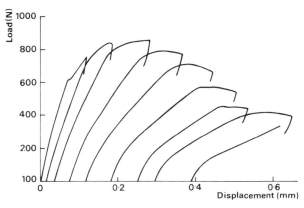

Fig. 16. Typical load/beam displacement result. Matrix with 2.5% glass fibre.

alumina cement or alkali-resistant glass and high alumina cement are shown in Fig. 13 (modulus of rupture) and Fig. 14 (impact strength), in both cases for water storage. These were obtained without any addition to the matrix, and improved results can be obtained in this way*.

A reasonable extrapolation of the data suggests little change in materials properties over a period of twenty years for alkali-resistant glass products used indoors or in sheltered positions. The benefits obtained with pfa addition, or by using high alumina cement, give encouragement that the technical problems of durability can be overcome to produce composites with adequate life even when continuously saturated.

Plain sheets of spray—suction composite containing 5.0% glass fibre complied with the requirements of BS 4036—66 for frost-resistance. None of the samples exposed to weathering for up to four years shows any signs of delamination or other frost attack.

5.6. Fracture toughness

This was measured [19] on premixed 2:1 OPC/pfa mixes with 0, 2.5 and 5% glass fibre by weight of the dry solids, and at ages (water curing) of 14, 28 and 84 days. The specimens were tested as beams $250 \times 38 \times 38$ mm under four-point loading. A notch 10 mm deep was sawn in the centre of the tension face and load and beam deflection were measured continuously, the load being increased in stages as a crack grew from the root of the notch. Figure 15 shows a typical load/displacement result for unreinforced matrix and Fig. 16 the result for a beam with 2.5% glass fibre. The crack depth was calculated from the compliance of the beam as determined

in the next loading cycle, and the critical stress intensity factor K_{IC} was calculated from the load and crack depth at any stage [20]. It was found that K_{IC} increased almost linearly with the crack growth and with fibre content and was little influenced by age at test. The apparent value of K_{IC} is given by $K_a = 0.4 + 0.025\, Cf$ where K_a is the apparent toughness in $MN/m^{3/2}$, C is the crack growth in mm and f is the fibre content, per cent of dry solids by weight.

If C is zero, $K_a = 0.4$, the value for unreinforced matrix, so that the toughness of the fibre reinforced material is no higher than that of the matrix at the initiation of crack growth, but thereafter increases with crack growth. This provides a mechanism for arresting crack growth and avoiding catastrophic failure.

5.7. Creep and fatigue

The creep properties of glass reinforced cement are broadly comparable with the creep properties of concrete, the glass fibre acting as a stiffener for the relatively high creep cement phase. There is no indication of any adverse creep effects in the composite resulting from the interaction between the matrix and the fibre and creep tests have shown no indication of any debonding problems.

Fatigue tests have also confirmed that the material will not present any special difficulties. Cycling in flexure between zero and a maximum stress less than the elastic limit provides a fatigue life of better than 10^6 cycles. Repeated flexure with peak stresses greater than the elastic limit results in earlier failure but typically a life of 10^4 cycles can be expected with peak stresses 60% of the ultimate. The fatigue properties of these composites are comparable with those of asbestos cement.

5.8. Fire resistance

Provided that the matrix itself is not too dense to allow the escape of combined water,

---

* Elkalite, a product of Elkalite Ltd., Ford Aerodrome, Arundel, Sussex, England.

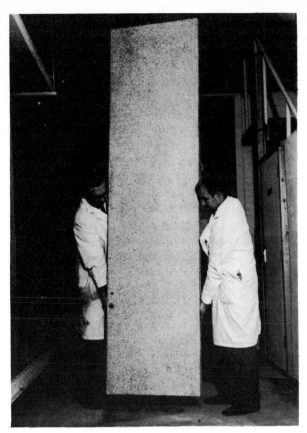

Fig. 17. Cladding panel 2.75 m high and 710 mm wide.

certain types of glass fibre reinforced composites have excellent fire resistance. Even when the matrix is completely dehydrated the fibrous reinforcement holds the matrix together and prevents flame penetration. A compacted neat cement matrix is too dense to allow water to evaporate and breaks down explosively but this can be prevented by modifying the matrix to reduce the density and the combined water content. For example, grc composites with a matrix of cement plus 40% pfa can be very resistant to fire. The reinforced concrete column described in Section 6, which has a 9 mm covering of permanent shuttering made with this type of grc, failed after 100 minutes under a load of 42 tonnes in the standard fire test. A control column without the composite cladding failed in 48 minutes. Another suitable matrix is autoclaved lime/silica. Boards, either 7 or 15 mm thick, of dry density 640 kg/m^3, tested as 1 m^2 samples to the requirements of BS 476, showed no flame penetration after one hour.

6. APPLICATIONS

A number of prototypes of components have been made at the Building Research Station to demonstrate the properties and potential uses of glass reinforced cement, and for test purposes. More than 100 firms are now actively engaged, under licence from Pilkington Brothers Limited, on the development of components and production methods, and several are already in commercial production.

The first components were made by the mechanised spray—suction process. The suction mould was used both to dewater the sprayed mix and, as a vacuum lifting pad, to transport the dewatered sheet to a pallet where it was folded to form some components, or wrapped around collapsible formers to make pipes or box sections.

Cladding panels 2.75 m high and 710 mm wide (Fig. 17) have been made from 9 mm sheet, containing 5% of glass fibre chopped to 34 mm lengths, by folding it to a shallow U section with jointing grooves formed in the 90 mm wide sides of the U. Each panel weighs only 50 kg, yet will withstand a wind pressure more than 50% greater than that of a 150 m.p.h. wind while spanning the full storey height. They can be made with various textured finishes.

The potential use for structural purposes has been demonstrated by using the same folding technique and mix to make hollow beams 360 mm wide and 200 mm deep with a wall thickness of 9 mm. Six of these beams formed the deck of the footbridge shown in Fig. 18, with two spans of 3.7 m. The supporting piles and beams were also made by folding glass reinforced cement sheet, and all have so far successfully withstood 18 months' exposure and wear. Tests on a single beam showed that the load at the elastic limit was equivalent to a uniformly distributed load of 5.4 kN/m^2, while the corresponding mid-span deflection was 6 mm. This deflection increased to 70 mm before the lower flanges of the beam failed in tension at a load equivalent to 13 kN/m^2.

A process of wrapping several layers of thin sheet around a collapsible timber former was used to make a box section, 200 mm square and 9 mm thick, which could be used as permanent shuttering to a conventional steel rod reinforced concrete column (Fig. 19). This greatly improved the fire resistance of the column, by delaying the spalling of concrete covering the corner bars, and details of this test are given in Subsection 5.8. In addition, this permanent shuttering provided a very smooth surface, suitable for immediate decoration, and additional protection against corrosion of the bars.

Pipes up to 200 mm in diameter have been made by a similar wrapping process, but the conventional spinning method has been found more suitable for larger pipes, since the mix is dewatered and compacted by centrifugal action. A 610 mm diameter pipe section (Fig. 20) has been made with a wall thickness of

Fig. 18. Prototype footbridge in glass fibre reinforced cement.

Fig. 19. Reinforced concrete column with permanent shuttering of glass reinforced cement.

Fig. 20. Centrifugally formed pipe; the spinning equipment is shown behind the pipe section.

Fig. 21. Window frame produced by injection moulding.

only 25 mm, of which the outer half was glass reinforced cement containing 5% of 34 mm fibre, while the inner half was a normal concrete mix. This pipe failed at a crown load of 44 kN per metre run when tested 28 days after casting.

The ability to make quite complex shapes by a form of injection moulding has been demonstrated by pumping a 1:1 cement/pfa mix containing 2.5% of 22 mm fibre into a closed mould to make the window frame shown in Fig. 21. Cladding panels in glass reinforced high alumina cement for high-rise flats have been developed by Elkalite Limited for the Greater London Council, and demonstrate the lightweight construction that can be achieved with such material. They are 64 mm thick sandwich panels, with a foamed plastic core, and weigh only 21 kg per square metre.

The high impact strength of the material has been demonstrated by the first commercial development of Portland cement and alkali-resistant glass fibre components. These ventilator shafts (Fig. 22), made by Trueflue Limited and now in use in the basement car park of a very large office block in Liverpool, have successfully withstood the impact of a car.

Fig. 22. Ventilator shaft in glass fibre reinforced cement (by courtesy of Trueflue Ltd. and Bingham Blades and Partners).

7. CONCLUSIONS

Glass fibre reinforced cement made from alkali-resistant glass fibre is a promising new material. A wide range of properties can be obtained, depending on the method of fabrication, the glass content and the formulation of the cement matrix. Its particular advantages are high impact resistance and fire resistance. Long-term strength tests and fatigue testing indicate that a satisfactory service life is attainable, although for continuously water-saturated conditions a pozzolanic addition to the cement matrix may be desirable.

ACKNOWLEDGEMENTS

The work described has been carried out as part of the research programme of the Building Research Establishment of the Department of the Environment, U.K., and Pilkington Brothers Limited of St Helens, Lancashire. Where no reference is given the data in this paper are taken from the unpublished work of several people engaged in the collaborative project. This paper is published by permission of the Director of the Building Research Establishment.

REFERENCES

1 E.G. Nawy, G.E. Neuwerth and G.J. Phillips, J. Struct. Div., Am. Soc. Civil Engrs., 97 (1970) 2203.
2 S. Kajfasz, Proc. Third Congr. Federation Intern. de Precontrainte, Berlin, 1958, Cement and Concrete Assoc., London, 1959, p. 436.
3 N.F. Soames, Mag. Concrete Res., 15 (1963) 151.
4 K.L. Biryukovich, Yu.L. Biryukovich and D.L. Biryukovich, Glass Fibre Reinforced Cement, Budivelnik, Kiev, 1964. Transl. No. 12, Civil Eng. Res. Assoc., London, 1966.
5 A.J. Majumdar and J.F. Ryder, Glass Technol., 9 (1968) 78.
6 A.J. Majumdar and J.F. Ryder, Sci. Ceram., 5 (1970) 539.
7 F.M. Lea, The Chemistry of Cement and Concrete, Arnold, London, 1970.
8 T.D. Robson, High Alumina Cement and Concrete, Contractors Record Ltd., London, 1962.
9 R. Hill, J. Mech. Phys. Solids, 11 (1963) 357.
10 H. Krenchel, Fibre Reinforcement, Akademisk Förlag, Copenhagen, 1964.
11 P. Lawrence, J. Mater. Sci., 7 (1972) 1.
12 V. Laws, J. Phys. D: Appl. Phys., 4 (1971) 1737.
13 R.C. de Vekey and A.J. Majumdar, Mag. Concrete Res., 20 (1968) 229.
14 R.C. de Vekey and A.J. Majumdar, J. Mater. Sci., 5 (1970) 183.
15 E. Kempster, Brit. Pat. Appl. 55419/69.
16 M.A. Ali and F.J. Grimer, J. Mater. Sci., 4 (1969) 389.
17 H.G. Allen, Proc. Intern. Building Exhibition Conf. on Prospects for Fibre-reinforced Construction Materials, Olympia, London, 24 November 1971. Building Research Station, Garston, Watford, 1971, p. 3.
18 B.R. Steele, Proc. Intern. Building Exhibition Conf. on Prospects for Fibre-reinforced Construction Materials, Olympia, London, 24 November 1971, Building Research Station, Garston, Watford, p. 29.
19 J.H. Brown, Mag. Concrete Res., 25 (1973) 31.
20 W.F. Brown and J.E. Srawley, Plane Strain Crack Toughness Testing of High Strength Metallic Materials, ASTM Spec. Tech. Publ. 410, 1969.

The role of the interface in glass fibre reinforced cement (CP 57/74)

A.J. Majumdar

INTRODUCTION

Interfaces are an integral part of the structure of composites and are therefore important in all phases of composite science and technology. The properties of the individual components of a composite are affected by the nature of their surfaces and this, in turn, has a significant influence on composite behaviour in fabrication and performance. However, a detailed characterisation of the interface of a composite from a materials point of view does not necessarily lead to a better interpretation of the macroscopic average properties of the composite. Practical correlations may emerge relating the texture of the interface to properties but in most cases a more fruitful assessment of the importance of interfacial effects is obtained from studies of the micromechanics of composite behaviour.

Glass fibre reinforced cement (GRC) provides an interesting example of interaction between a brittle fibre and a brittle matrix. The matrix is porous, particulate, highly alkaline and its physical properties change with time. Inorganic silicate glasses are notoriously unstable in an alkaline medium and it is to be expected, therefore, that the interfacial region in GRC will remain active for a long time. In this system the interface is perhaps best considered not as a two-dimensional bounding surface across which some type of discontinuity occurs but as a zone whose thickness depends on environmental conditions and across which a more or less rapid transition in properties takes place from that of the fibre to that of the matrix. Because of the particulate nature of the matrix, this zone is heterogeneous in character, the fibre/matrix contact points being separated by voids and also pores in the matrix in an irregular way. The materials properties of this zone may alter with age.

As a material, GRC is not unlike asbestos cement. Glass fibres have strengths similar to that of asbestos fibres and they have the additional advantage of being available in long (even continuous) lengths. Unfortunately conventional glass fibres lose their strength quite rapidly when placed in the cement matrix but developments over the last few years have shown that it is possible to produce much more alkali resistant fibres. As a result of collaboration between the Building Research Station and Pilkington Bros Ltd, a new generation of glass fibres 'Cem-Fil'* has become available for cement reinforcement. The durability of composites prepared with this glass fibre and ordinary Portland cement has been studied over the last few years at BRS and in the laboratories of Pilkington Bros Ltd and this programme of work is continuing. A summary of the important achievements of this collaborative effort has been given by Steele (1972). Certain features of the interface in these cement-based composites have been revealed in this work, and constitute the subject matter of this paper.

THEORETICAL CONSIDERATIONS

Most theoretical investigations of composite properties are based on the assumption of a perfect bond between fibre and matrix and several comprehensive reviews of the solutions available have been made recently (see for instance Kelly (1966) or Holister and Thomas (1966)). The elastic modulus E_c and the strength σ_c of the composite are described by 'mixture rules' which are based on the assumption that the fibres support stress only along their longitudinal axes. Thus

$$E_c = \eta_o \, \eta_\ell \, E_f \, V_f + E_m \, V_m$$

and

$$\sigma_c = \eta_o' \, \eta'_\ell \, \sigma_f \, V_f + \sigma_m \, V_m$$

where η_o, η_o' and η_ℓ, η'_ℓ are efficiency factors for orientation and length respectively.
E, σ and V refer to the elastic modulus, average tensile strength and volume fraction and the subscripts c, f and m refer to the composite, fibre and matrix respectively.
Krenchel (1964) has derived efficiency factors for various fibre orientations for the calculation

---

*   Registered trade-mark of Pilkington Brothers Limited

of E_c. For composites reinforced with discontinuous fibres, the concept of a 'critical length' defined as:

$$\ell_c = \frac{\sigma_f d}{2\tau_i}$$

where d is the diameter of the fibre and τ_i the shear strength of the interface, has been particularly valuable. The ratio of the fibre length to the critical length is important; short fibres will tend to be pulled out of the composite during fracture while long fibres will be broken.

Very recently Laws (1971) has suggested combined efficiency factors of length and orientation for the calculation of composite strength. In this analysis, the combined or total efficiency factor describes the proportion of the ultimate fibre stress that is utilised when the composite fails by fibre failure and/or pull-out.

For calculating the strength of thin composites produced from brittle matrices and random discontinuous reinforcing fibres (eg glass fibre reinforced cement and gypsum products) Allen (1972) has proposed a theory in which no assumptions are made about the magnitude or the distribution of bond stresses. It is necessary, however, to know the relationship between the length of embedment of a fibre and the force needed to break it or pull it out. The mechanical properties of glass fibre reinforced cement (GRC) and gypsum plaster (GRG) have also been examined by Aveston, Cooper and Kelly (1972) in the light of their new theory on single and multiple fracture. These systems provide classic examples of composite materials in which the failure strain of the matrix is much smaller than that of the fibre. Such composites fail by multiple fracture, beyond a minimum volume fraction of fibres.

The length efficiency factors η_ℓ and η'_ℓ depend on the transfer of stress between fibre and matrix across the interface and hence on the properties of the interface. Approximate shear lag analysis (Greszczuk, 1969) has been used to derive the tensile stress in the fibre and the shear stress at the interface. The maximum shear stress is developed at the ends of the fibres; when the maximum stress reaches the shear strength of the interface, the two components debond and the transfer of stress then depends on the frictional stresses at the interface. At the end of the elastic region, cracks form in the matrix and the load is thrown onto the fibres bridging the crack. If there are sufficient fibres to support the stress, the matrix cracking continues until the distance between cracks is too small to allow the transfer of stress sufficient to break the matrix further. The strength of the composite depends on the maximum stress an array of fibres held across a major crack can support.

Lawrence (1972) has derived expressions for the maximum load required to debond fully a fibre from an elastic matrix assuming that there is a static frictional force between the surfaces after the interface has failed in shear. Laws, Lawrence and Nurse (1973) have used these expressions to derive the maximum load a fibrous mat can support and hence to predict the combined orientation and length efficiency factor for a composite containing a random planar distribution of short fibres. The results of the analysis suggest that the shear stresses developed break the 'intrinsic' interfacial bond and the important parameters determining the strength of the composites are fibre length and the static and dynamic frictional stresses at the interface.

The role that the shear strength of the interface in a fibre-reinforced composite material plays in determining its behaviour under conditions of impact is rather complicated but this has been treated recently in a very comprehensive way by Cooper and Kelly (1969) and by Aveston, Cooper and Kelly (1972). The latter publication deals with the case of energy absorption processes in composites exhibiting multiple fracture (eg glass fibre reinforced cement and plaster) and the reader is referred to this work for a proper appreciation of the subject. The general comment that is relevant here is that the conditions contributing to the work of fracture which derive from the failure of the bond or by fibre pull-out are found to depend on the diameter of the fibre and the strength of the interfacial bond. In cases where some fibres break, an increase in fibre diameter or decrease in the strength of the bond between fibre and matrix leads to an increase in the work of fracture. This prediction seems to have been borne out in most cases.

FABRICATION OF THE COMPOSITE

The properties of a fibre reinforced composite depend to a large extent on fabrication and the interface plays a most significant role here. Many composites do not attain the level of strength or other properties expected of them from theoretical considerations of the properties of their constituents because the interface in these materials is not optimally developed. GRC composites, the properties of which are discussed in later sections, have all been manufactured by a special method developed at the Building Research Station (Majumdar and Ryder 1968; British Patent 1, 204, 541).

This method employs a spraying technique similar to the process used in the plastics industry for glass fibre reinforcement. In order to incorporate glass fibres in cements, it is necessary to start with a slurry having a high water/solid ratio and then remove by either suction or pressing most of the water surplus to that required for proper hardening of the binder phase.

The BRS spray-suction method, which has recently been mechanised, uses a glass-chopper mounted on a spray-gun which is attached to a pump. Streams of chopped rovings and cement slurry meet and a combined spray is distributed over the surface of a perforated metal mould. When the pre-determined thickness has been built up, the top surface is levelled and the excess water is extracted by the application of suction. In this method it is possible to select the length of reinforcement required and up to 10 vol% of chopped glass fibre can be incorporated in the matrix without any difficulty. Composites whose properties are discussed in this paper were prepared having a 4.0 vol% of glass fibre of 34 mm length.

The composite produced by the spray-suction technique appears to have a structure in which the fibres are randomly distributed in the plane of the sheet.

MICROSTRUCTURE OF THE COMPOSITE

It is important to point out that in the present method of manufacture, the reinforcing element may either be a fibre bundle (consisting of say 204 filaments) or the individual filaments of the bundle, the degree of filamentisation of a strand being governed by the nature of the coating applied on the glass fibre during manufacture in order to protect it against mechanical damage. The degree of filamentisation of the bundle has a significant influence on all interfacial effects and these will control the micro and the macro-mechanics of the composite. The freshly fractured surface of a GRC composite is shown in Figure 1*, which is a scanning electron micrograph. It is apparent that in this case the glass fibre 'strand' had not lost its integrity during manufacture of the composite. Figure 2 shows another scanning electron micrograph of a GRC specimen where the fibre strand had broken down into individual filaments.

BOND STRENGTH

In a particulate matrix like cement the bond between the matrix and the reinforcing fibre is bound to be discontinuous. This is true for filamentising as well as integral type of fibre bundle.

Figure 1 Glass fibre strand as the reinforcing element

Figure 2 Glass fibre filament as the reinforcing element

---

*Unless otherwise stated the individual glass filaments in the photographs are approximately 10 μm in diameter.

Scanning electron micrographs of composite materials help to distinguish them in terms of their interface. Figure 3 is a micrograph of glass fibre reinforced plastics. The reinforcement is seen to be completely bonded to the matrix. Glass fibres in gypsum plaster (Figure 4) on the other hand only make intermittent contact with the matrix through recrystallised gypsum crystals. Glass fibre in cement is an intermediate case.

In GRC, the bond which is established between the fibre and the matrix is continuous in places and appears to be firm. In the micrograph in Figure 5 a separation is seen, but this is partly due to the cylindrical nature of the fibre and might also have been caused while preparing the specimen. However, taking a fibre bundle as such, there does not seem to be adequate penetration of the bundle by the matrix. In asbestos cement, primarily due to its method of manufacture and perhaps because of the surface properties of the fibre, wetting of the fibre bundle by the cement slurry appears to be much more effective. Again, scanning electron micrographs illustrate this point very well.

In Figure 6 a bundle of asbestos fibres removed from a freshly fractured commercially

Figure 3   Interfacial bond in glass fibre reinforced plastics

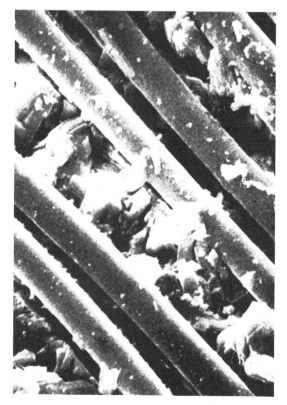

Figure 4   Interfacial bond in glass fibre
reinforced gypsum plaster

Figure 5   Interfacial bond in glass fibre
reinforced cement

produced asbestos cement sheet is shown. The Ca X-ray image obtained from an energy-dispersive X-ray analyser attached to the scanning electron microscope (SEM) is shown in Figure 7. Chrysotile asbestos generally contains little if any Ca and the preponderance of Ca shown in Figure 7 associated with the asbestos bundle is due to products of hydration of cement on or inside the fibre bundle.

Some idea of the strength of the bond between glass fibre and cement or plaster can be obtained by 'pull-out' tests. In a series of experiments 'pull-out' stresses of 0.5mm diameter glass rods have been determined by de Vekey and Majumdar (1968) employing various materials as matrices. Some of the results are given in Table 1. Although there may be uncertainties about the absolute values of these bond strength determinations, the relative order in the case of different matrices is believed to be correct. And this is important when attempting to understand the performance of a composite material under conditions of shock loading.

One important aspect of the interfacial bond between glass fibre and Portland cement is that its strength increases with time. Taking an alkali resistant glass as an example, this time-dependence of the bond strength has been studied by de Vekey and Majumdar (1970) under different environmental conditions and their results are shown in Figure 8. If the water/solid ratio of the matrix were varied, its porosity would change and so would the magnitude of the interfacial bond strength.

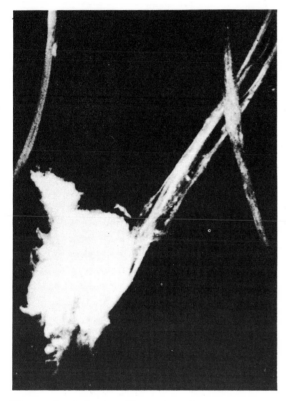

Figure 6 Asbestos fibres in asbestos cement

Figure 7 Ca X-ray image of asbestos fibres in asbestos cement

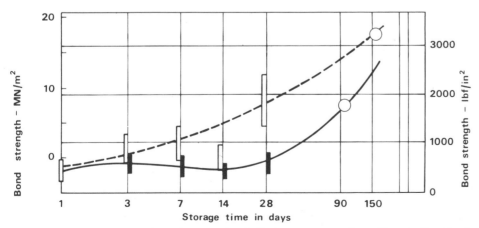

Figure 8 Development of bond strength of alkali-resistant glass fibre in Portland cement paste. —— water cured; ---- air (100% rh) cured; ○ bond strength greater than these values

Table 1 Bond strength in composite materials

Matrix	Fibre	Curing conditions	Bond strength (MN m^{-2})	Coefficient of variation (%)
Portland cement paste	E-glass	28 days in moist air at 25°C	6. 38	32. 0
Portland cement paste	E-glass	28 days in water at 25°C	9. 25	27. 5
Hemihydrate plaster (Crystocal)	E-glass	24 h at 40°C (water/plaster = 0. 3)	6. 76	14. 0
50/50 mixture of Crystocal and plaster of Paris	E-glass	24 h at 40°C (water/plaster = 0. 3)	5. 59	13. 0
Plaster of Paris	E-glass	24 h at 40°C (water/plaster = 0. 5)	1. 00	14. 5
Polyester resin (crystic 195)	E-glass	24 h at 40°C	>15. 60*	23. 0
Polyester resin (crystic 189)	surface-coated E-glass	unknown	3. 68	36. 0
Polyester resin	surface-coated E-glass	unknown	>20. 70*	–
Portland cement paste	bright high-tensile steel wire	28 days in air at 25°C	11. 00	35. 0
Portland cement paste	bright high-tensile steel wire	28 days in water at 25°C	5. 54	45. 0
Portland cement concrete	mild steel	28 days (water/cement = 0. 6)	4. 75	–
Portland cement concrete	rusty mild steel	70 days (water/cement = 0. 6)	6. 00	–
Portland cement paste	rusty high-tensile steel wire	28 days in moist air	10. 39	37. 0
Portland cement paste	chrysotile asbestos	unknown	0. 83	–
Portland cement paste	crocidolite asbestos	unknown	3. 17	–

*Specimens failed before fibre pulled out.

Of course, when an integral strand is the reinforcing element, bond strength should be measured using the multi-filament bundles of glass fibre. Such a technique is being developed (Laws, Lawrence and Nurse 1973) and initial results with gypsum plaster are now available. The sample consists of 16 fibre strands mounted in parallel in a block of plaster (Figure 9). An artificial crack is produced in the specimen by the dividers which also serve to keep the fibres in position during casting. Typical pull-out curves are shown in Figure 10.

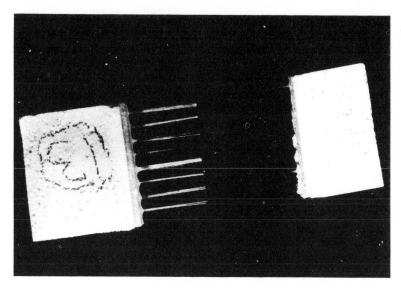

Figure 9   Photo of a multiple strand pull-out specimen

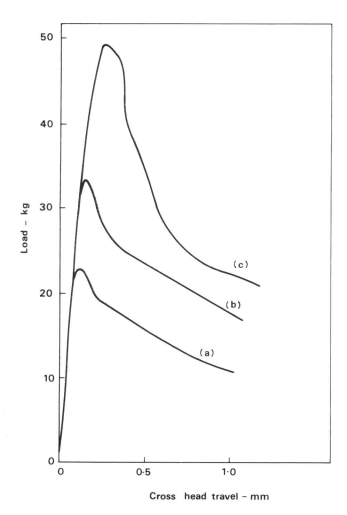

Cross head travel – mm

Figure 10 Multi-fibre pull-out curves, glass fibre strands in gypsum plaster (water/plaster ratio 0.5). Embedded lengths were (a) 4 mm; (b) 6.5 mm and (c) 13 mm.

The maximum load reached is an average for the 16 strands since some strands begin to slip while others do not. The average load refers to the stress required for the strands to slip and therefore depends on the 'static' bond at the interface. In some cases (eg in GRC) this bond could include an intrinsic or chemical bond as well as a static frictional term. The slope of the 'pull-out' curves after all the strands have begun to slip depends on the dynamic frictional stresses at the interface. The slope is not constant, possibly because the strand does not remain integral as it is pulled out. On average, the ratio of dynamic frictional bond to 'static' bond for glass strands in gypsum plaster (water to solid ratio 0.5) is about 0.7 at pull-out lengths such that no fibres break. As the pull-out length increases some fibres break and this ratio decreases. Even when all strands break, there is still an appreciable dynamic frictional term as the filaments in the strand separate.

Because of the non-uniformity of the geometry of fibre strands, it is not practicable to calculate interfacial bond strengths from these measurements in a way similar to that used for values in Table 1. Maximum stresses that can be supported by definite embedded lengths of fibre are, however, easily obtained and these values can be used for calculating strength of composites.

COMPOSITE PROPERTIES

Typical properties of glass fibre and a cement-based matrix relevant to this paper are given in Table 2.

Table 2 Properties of components

Material	Elastic modulus $(GN\,m^{-2})$	Compressive strength $(MN\,m^{-2})$	Tensile strength $(MN\,m^{-2})$	Modulus of rupture $(MN\,m^{-2})$	Tensile fracture strain (%)
Hardened cement paste	7 – 28	14 – 140	1.4 – 7	2.8 – 14	0.02 – 0.06
Glass fibre	70 – 75	–	1750 – 2100	–	2 – 3

Material	Poisson ratio	Thermal expansion $(10^{-6}\,K^{-1})$	Volume change on drying (%)	Density $(g\,cm^{-3})$
Hardened cement paste	0.23 – 0.30	12 – 20	0.2 – 0.3 (negative)	1.7 – 2.2
Glass fibre	0.22	5 – 7	–	2.5 – 2.6

The durability of GRC composites is being studied by examining the change in their mechanical properties as a function of time of storage under different conditions. The properties which have been routinely measured in this study are:

1   The load to failure in a four point bending test. The 'modulus of rupture' has been calculated from the maximum value of the load, assuming the conventional elastic formula.

2   Impact strength using a simple IZOD machine.

Although there is no fully acceptable model for the explanation of modulus of rupture in brittle matrix/brittle fibre composites, this test was preferred as a measure of the mechanical strengths of the composites because of the known difficulty of determining the tensile strengths of brittle materials.

The composite boards were cut into samples immediately after fabrication and stored under the appropriate conditions. As is common with materials of this type, there is a considerable variability in the value of any mechanical property as measured on samples which should be 'identical'. Property measurements have all been made on randomly selected samples from these boards and testing of large numbers has resulted in 90% confidence limits to correspond in most instances to approximately $\pm$ 7% of the mean in the case of modulus of rupture and $\pm$ 14% of the mean in the case of impact strength.

Some idea of the long-term durability of GRC composites based on ordinary Portland cement and two glass fibres produced from boro-silicate E-glass and a zirconosilicate glass can be obtained from Figures 11 and 12. For convenience in assembling the data, strength values have been plotted against the logarithm of the time of storage although there is no known theoretical basis for such a relationship. It is clear from the figures that GRC composites produced from an alkali-resistant glass show a much better long-term retention of strength than those made with E-glass fibres.

The effect of adding a reactive silicate material to the cement capable of combining with $Ca(OH)_2$ on the properties of GRC has also been studied. Such materials are well known to the con-

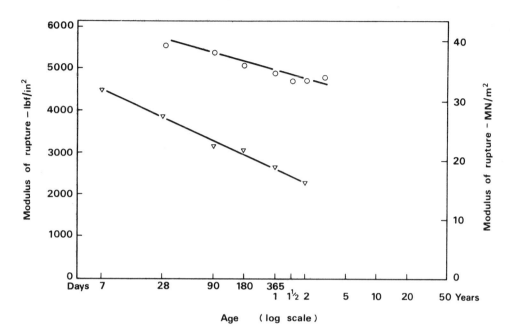

Figure 11 Relation between modulus of rupture and age of glass fibre reinforced Portland cement composites. ○ Alkali-resistant glass; ▽ E-glass.

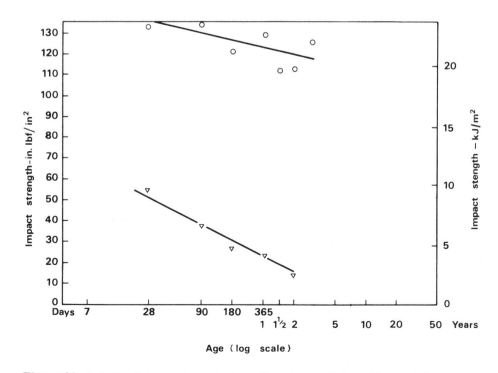

Figure 12 Relation between impact strength and age of glass fibre reinforced Portland cement composites. ○ Alkali-resistant glass; ▽E-glass.

struction industry, the one chosen in this study being pulverised fuel ash (pfa); Figures 13 and 14 show the results obtained with a matrix comprising 60% by weight of ordinary Portland cement and 40% by weight of pfa. Two storage conditions, namely in air of 40% rh at 18°C and under water, also at 18°C, have been used. Comparative results obtained with an alkali resistant glass and E-glass are given in Figures 13 and 14 for modulus of rupture and impact strength respectively. Although the strength results are seemingly more variable when pfa is added as a diluent to the cement, it is nevertheless clear from the figures that for this matrix also the alkali resistant glass performs much better than E-glass from the point of view of the long-term durability of GRC composites.

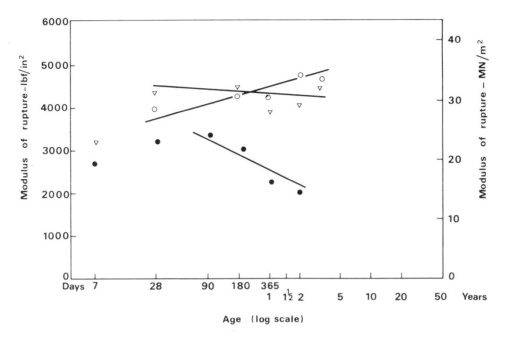

Figure 13 Relation between modulus of rupture and age of glass fibre reinforced
Portland cement composites containing pfa. ▽Alkali-resistant glass, in
air; ○Alkali-resistant glass, in water; ●E-glass, in water

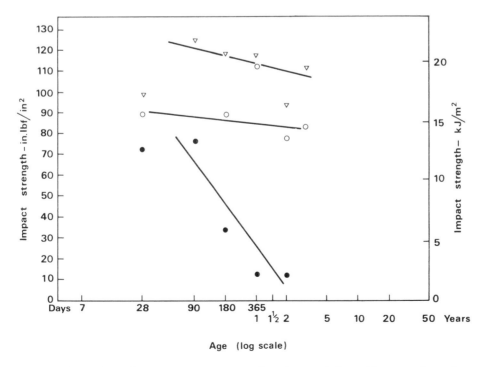

Figure 14 Relation between impact strength and age of glass fibre reinforced
Portland cement composites containing pfa. ▽Alkali-resistant glass,
in air; ○Alkali-resistant glass, in water; ●E-glass, in water.

Typical stress-strain diagrams for the GRC composite material containing approximately
4.0 vol% glass fibre and cured for 28 days and tested in tension are shown schematically in
Figure 15a for two curing conditions. The stress-strain curves consist of two parts:
(a) a linear elastic portion which terminates when the matrix cracks and (b) quasi-plastic region
which begins at the elastic limit and extends up to ultimate failure. In the quasi-plastic region,
the load is carried predominantly by the fibre and progressive debonding at the fibre/matrix
interface takes place; slippage of one fibre over another is also possible. A possible explanation
for the general shape of the durability graphs shown in Figures 11 - 14 is that initially failure is
due to fibre pull-out because of the low bond strengths between the fibres and the matrix. As
bond improves, fibres fail before they pull out; this improvement may or may not indicate
chemical attack on the fibre.

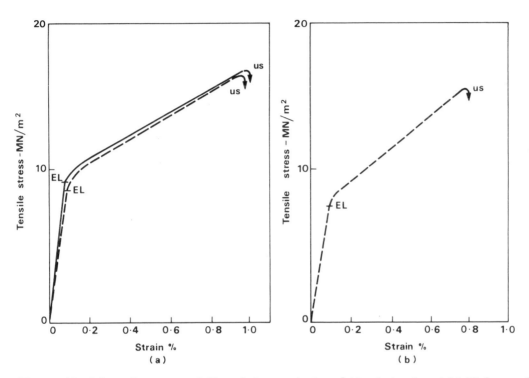

Figure 15 Schematic representation of stress-strain relation in tension at (a) 28 days and
(b) one year. ---- Air stored: —— water stored.
EL = elastic limit; US = ultimate strength.

INTERFACE PHENOMENA

In order to understand the time-dependent behaviour of GRC composites it is instructive to
consider their constituent phases separately and to attempt to suggest some likely interfacial
phenomena from these considerations. The bending strength of a cement paste with a water to
cement ratio of 0.3 has been measured at various ages and the value has been found to remain
approximately constant up to one year after an initial rise. The physiochemical nature of paste,
however, changes during this period. Initially, the hydration products of cement assume a
colloidal form, the calcium silicate hydrates showing no evidence of crystallinity upon X-ray
examination. With time, the cement gel becomes more crystalline causing the paste to become
possibly more brittle with decreased porosity. With such a low water to cement ratio, a substantial amount of cement will remain unhydrated. When this comes into contact with water it
will produce large quantities of $Ca(OH)_2$ crystals many of which will assume fairly large size if
allowed to grow. The aqueous phase in contact with set cement paste will always remain alkaline,
the pH of the solution being potentially that of a saturated solution of $Ca(OH)_2$. It is the interaction
between this alkaline paste and the glass fibre which controls the properties of the interface and
hence those of the composites.

CHEMICAL REACTIONS AT THE INTERFACE

The silicate glass fibres placed in the cement matrix are reactive towards the alkali and
alkaline earth hydroxides produced during cement hydration and the effect of this interaction on
the strength of the fibre is of crucial importance in determining the durability of GRC composites.
The advantages of a soda-silica-zirconia glass fibre over that of the borosilicate E-glass were
first demonstrated by Majumdar and Ryder (1968) who measured the tensile strength of these

fibres after digesting them with a 'cement effluent' solution at 80°C. The strength of the corroded fibres was, in many cases, so low that a special technique (Gillett and Majumdar, 1968) had to be developed for testing them for strength. These results are reproduced in Figure 16.

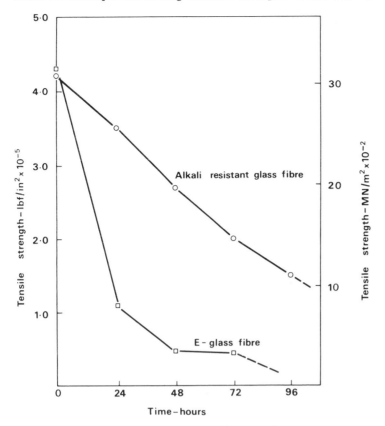

Figure 16 Tensile strength of glass fibres in the aqueous
solution phase of Portland Cement at 80°C

Attempts have been made to understand, from a chemical point of view, the reasons for the superior performance of the alkali-resistant glass fibre in Portland cements vis-à-vis fibres of E-glass. Fibres of the two glasses were drawn as uncoated single filaments of approximately 9μm diameter using a furnace assembly already described (de Vekey and Majumdar, 1967). They were immersed in cement extract solutions for various periods of time at various temperatures and the extent of glass breakdown was determined by analyses of the solution phase and an acid wash solution used to remove any alkali insoluble reaction products from the fibre surface.

Analytical difficulties, particularly with the determination of silica removed from E-glass, precluded a direct comparison of the extent of network breakdown in the two glasses. Since the amount of B_2O_3 extracted from E-glass increased systematically with time and temperature, this element was used as a measure of the network breakdown. In Figure 17 are plotted the amounts of (B_2O_3 + Al_2O_3 + SiO_2) extracted from E-glass assuming that all three glass components are extracted at the same rate, ie Al_2O_3 and SiO_2 are proportional to the B_2O_3 measured. Curves for data obtained after reaction at 80°C, 65°C and 50°C are presented. The total amounts of (SiO_2 + Al_2O_3 + ZrO_2) removed from the zirconosilicate glass at the various times are also shown in Figure 17.

The graphs in Figure 17 show that the attack on E-glass is initially very rapid and then tails off at longer times, whereas the reaction with the alkali resistant glass is slow and increases very little with time. This difference in the rates of alkali attack would be even greater if the solution pH had been maintained at the original value throughout the series of experiments. Figure 18 shows that with E-glass the solution pH drops rapidly and then levels off somewhat. This levelling off at the lower pH corresponds to the reduction in the rate of attack noted in Figure 17. For the zirconosilicate glass, the pH remains high but still the chemical attack appears to be minimal.

Methods have recently been developed by which glass strands can be removed from GRC composite specimens and the strength of single filaments measured. This is facilitated by the relative ease with which the composite specimens can be cleaved parallel to the plane of the board and the fibre strands exposed. After a short acid treatment the fibres can be peeled away

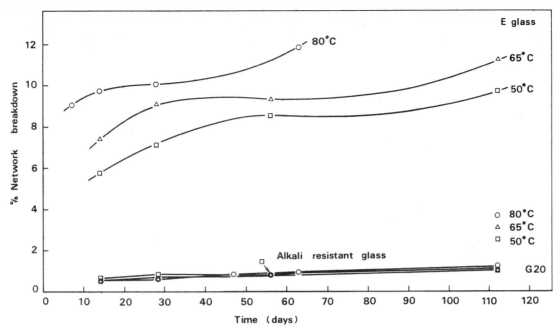

Figure 17 Network breakdown of glass in a cement extract solution

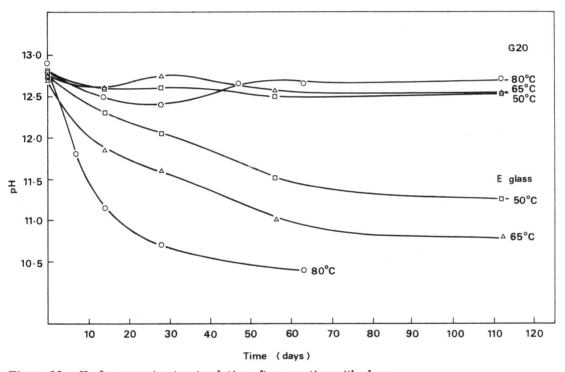

Figure 18 pH of a cement extract solution after reaction with glass.

from the matrix and the adhering materials removed. The tensile strength of these fibres extracted from composite specimens stored over various lengths of time has been determined and the results have been plotted in Figure 19 with 90% confidence limits. For comparison the results obtained with a reference sample are also given. The consistency of the strength results of the reference sample indicate that the solutions used to remove and wash the fibres had little or no effect on the filament strength.

The graphs in Figure 19 show that even after two years storage in laboratory air the glass fibres extracted from composites are remarkably strong as reinforcement and this retention of strength on the part of individual filaments accounts for the superior performance of GRC composites made with the alkali resistant glass fibre (Figures 11 to 14).

The Portland cement matrix, as is well known, remains highly alkaline throughout its entire life in water storage and it is to be expected that when a glass fibre is placed in this environment the glass/matrix interface will remain active for a long time. When a reactive silicate material such as pfa is added to the matrix, concentrations of Ca^{++} and OH^- in the solution phase are reduced which, in turn, produces a favourable influence on the stability of the interface.

The bending strength of these composites at early ages is lower than those having no pfa, partly because the matrix of cement plus pfa is weaker than the plain cement itself, but more probably due to a slower development of the interfacial bond in a less corrosive medium. If a cement which is less corrosive than ordinary Portland cement is used, the durability of the GRC composite made from it would be expected to be better than the results summarised in Figures 11 and 12. Work in progress in this Laboratory with high-alumina cement, which has been briefly reported previously (Steele 1972), confirms this view.

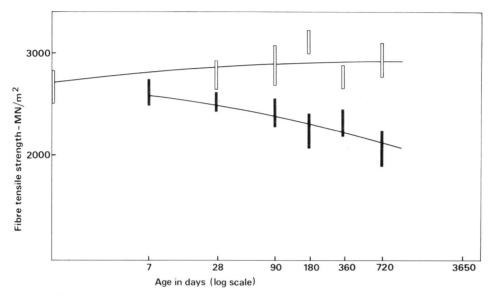

Figure 19   Tensile strength of glass fibres removed from GRC composites.
❙ fibres from the board;   ❑ reference sample.

PHYSICAL EFFECTS AT THE INTERFACE

Compared with bulk glass all glass fibres have much higher tensile strength because of the relative flawlessness of their surface. When these fibres are placed in a slurry of cement, surface flaws are generated or existing flaws are deepened by the combined effect of attrition by the clinker particles and chemical corrosion by the solution phase. Some evidence of this degradation suffered by certain types of glass fibres has been obtained with the help of the scanning electron microscope. Figure 20 shows an SEM photograph of the surface of an uncoated alkali resistant glass fibre reacted at ambient temperature for 126 days with the extract obtained by continuously shaking an ordinary Portland cement with water for 16 days. No indication of damage is visible. When borosilicate E-glass fibres are subjected to a similar treatment, evidence of pronounced attack is easily seen (Figure 21).

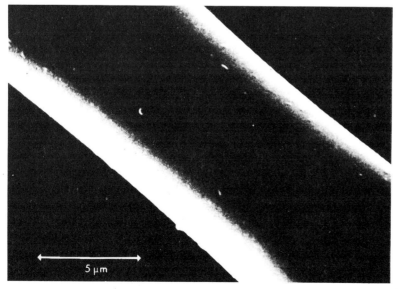

Figure 20   Surface of an alkali-resistant glass fibre reacted with a
cement extract solution

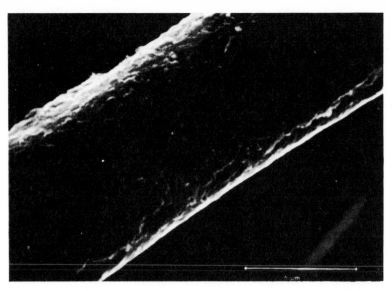

Figure 21 Surface of E-glass fibre reacted with a cement extract solution

Figure 22 is an interesting illustration of an extreme form of attack on a silicate glass fibre. The solution used was N/1 NaOH and the fibres were digested with it at 50°C for 100 days. It is quite apparent that a reaction layer had formed on the surface of the fibre which subsequently detached itself from the bulk.

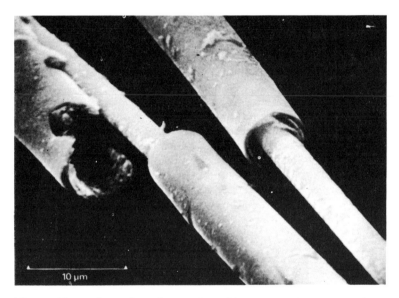

Figure 22 Surface of a silicate glass fibre reacted with a hot caustic soda solution

As a consequence of surface degradation ordinary glass fibres become weaker with time when placed in a cement environment and possibilities exist that the submicroscopic 'etch pits' provide locations for nucleation and growth of crystalline phases. The interfacial zone is thus modified as a result of attack on the fibres. A degree of stability in the interfacial zone is necessary however if the improved properties of GRC composites are to be retained. One way of achieving this is by using highly alkali-resistant glass fibres.

The tensile cracking strain of the neat cement paste is in the region 0.02 to 0.08%, the exact value depending on several variables, notably the water to cement ratio of the paste and its age which controls the degree of hydration. When 4.0 vol% of an alkali resistant fibre is added to the matrix, it can be seen from Figure 15 that the strain at the elastic limit of the composite is similar to that of the neat cement paste but at failure a 28 day old composite has shown a strain of 1.0%. This high value of strain is associated with the multiple cracking of the matrix and the debonding and pull-out of fibres, phenomena which impart to GRC composites a very satisfactory impact resistance.

It had been mentioned previously that the impact strength of GRC composites is reduced slightly with age, a phenomenon well known in asbestos cement products. This may be due more to the increase in the interfacial bond strength than to the loss in the tensile strength suffered by the fibre. Comparing Figure 15a with Figure 15b it can be seen that the ultimate failure strain of GRC reduces to 0.7% after one year. Even this value is higher, by more than an order of magnitude, than the failure strain of the matrix and explains why the high impact strength of GRC composites is retained in air storage (Figure 12).

A still better performance in impact resistance is obtained when a pozzolanic material such as pfa is added to the cement (Figure 14). The precise mechanism by which this improvement is secured is not understood yet but obviously the microstructure at the interface plays an important role here. The reactive silicate material combines very effectively with $Ca(OH)_2$ produced by the hydrated cement and it is thought that the physiochemical nature of the reaction product has a significant influence on the properties of the interface.

However, it is the view of the present author that a fall, however small, is to be expected in the impact strength of fibre reinforced cement products over a period of years. Experience of the asbestos cement industry lends support to this view. In addition to the increase in the strength of the bond between fibres and cement, it is also possible that the calcium silicate hydrate gel produced in large amounts when cement hydrates becomes less porous with time because of its tendency to crystallise. The gel must necessarily be a major constituent of the interfacial zone in view of its enormous surface area ($\sim 200 \, m^2/g$) and any loss in its deformability may contribute adversely to the fracture toughness of the composite material.

CONCLUSIONS

Glass fibre reinforced cement is proving to be a new and versatile composite material for the construction industry. When an alkali resistant glass fibre is used, the bending strength of the composite shows an initial increase over a period of months and then a slight reduction in strength is observed. The magnitude of the decrease in strength is dependent on the conditions used in storing the material and there are indications that this trend is absent when pfa is included in the mix.

The strength results are interpretable in qualitative terms on the basis of the changes taking place in the interfacial zone between the fibre and the matrix. These changes are brought about by the interaction of the glass fibre with the cement matrix as well as the continued hydration of the cement itself. Chemical bonds may form between the fibre and the matrix but significant contributions to the bond strength are also made by static and dynamic frictional forces at the interface. These factors, together with multiple cracking of the matrix, control the mechanical properties of composites such as glass fibre reinforced cement.

ACKNOWLEDGEMENT

The author wishes to thank his colleagues, Miss V Laws, Dr K Speakman and Mr M A Ali for many helpful suggestions and comments.

REFERENCES

Allen, H G. J Phys D: Appl Phys, Vol 5, p 331 (1972).

Aveston, J, Cooper, G A and Kelly, A. Proc Conf Properties of fibre composites, National Physical Laboratory, 4 November 1971; IPC Science and Technology Press, Guildford, pp 15-26 (1972).

British Patent 1, 204, 541. National Research and Development Corporation, London (1970).

Cooper, G A and Kelly, A. Interfaces in composites, ASTM Special Technical Publication STP 452, pp 90-106 (1969).

de Vekey, R C and Majumdar, A J. J Sci Instrum, Vol 44, p 864 (1967).

de Vekey, R C and Majumdar, A J. Mag Concr Res, Vol 20, p 229 (1968).

de Vekey, R C and Majumdar, A J. J Mater Sci, Vol 5, p 183 (1970).

Gillett, R S and Majumdar, A J. Apparatus for testing tensile strengths of corroded glass fibres. Building Research Station Current Paper CP 26/68 (1968).

Greszczuk, L B. Interfaces in composites, ASTM Special Technical Publication STP 452, pp 42–58 (1969).

Holister, G S and **Thomas, C.** Fibre-reinforced Materials, Elsevier Publishing Company, Amsterdam (1966).

Kelly, A. Strong Solids, Clarendon Press, Oxford (1966).

Krenchel, H. Fibre Reinforcement, Akademisk Forlag, Copenhagen (1964).

Lawrence, P. J Mater Sci, Vol 7, p 1 (1972).

Laws, V. J Phys D: Appl Phys Vol 4, p 1737 (1971).

Laws, V, Lawrence, P and **Nurse, R W.** Reinforcement of brittle matrices by glass fibres, J Phys D: Appl Phys, Vol 6, p 523 (1973).

Majumdar, A J and **Ryder, J F.** Glass Technol, Vol 9, p 78 (1968).

Steele, B R. Proc Intern Bldg Conf, Prospects for fibre reinforced construction materials, Olympia, London, 24 November 1971. Building Research Station, Garston, pp 29–39 (1972).

Steel fibre reinforced concrete (CP 69/74)

J. Edgington, D.J. Hannant and R.I.T. Williams

Definitions of terms relating to fibre reinforced concrete

The composite   The total constituents, ie cement paste, air void, aggregate and fibres.

Matrix   That part of the composite which is not occupied by the fibres.

Fibre aspect ratio   Fibre length/fibre diameter.

Fibre volume fraction $\dfrac{\text{volume of fibres}}{\text{volume of the composite}}$.

1   INTRODUCTION

At various intervals since the turn of the century short pieces of steel have been included within concrete in an attempt to endow the material with greater tensile strength and ductility. It was not, however, until 1963 when Romualdi and Batson[1] published the results of an investigation carried out in the USA on steel fibre reinforced concretes that any substantial interest was shown either by research organisations or by the construction industry. The claims made by Romualdi and Batson and subsequently by the Battelle Development Corporation[2], who filed a patent for the material later known as Wirand, were far reaching. In the development of the theory, it was assumed that concrete was a notch sensitive medium in which one could calculate the critical flaw size. It was claimed that the addition of short randomly distributed fibres to concrete would elevate the tensile cracking to at least 6.9 MN/m^2 (1000 lbf/in^2) when the average spacing of the included fibres was less than 7.6 mm. These claims aroused interest since, if the composite properties were as claimed, steel fibre reinforcement would provide a solution to the problem of tensile cracking that had for so long been an intrinsic deficiency of concrete.

It was with the intention of assessing both the validity of the claims and the viability of steel fibre reinforced concrete for use by the construction industry in this country that the Department of the Environment provided finance for this investigation. The main objectives were to assess the characteristics of the material during production and in the hardened state when incorporating various types and concentrations of steel fibres within cement pastes, mortars and concretes. A typical sample of steel fibre reinforced concrete is shown in Figure 1.

The detailed findings have been submitted to the Department of the Environment in a research report[3] and the aim of this paper is to present a summary of the work so that the knowledge

Figure 1   Typical sample of steel fibre reinforced concrete

gained regarding steel fibre reinforced concrete mixes is made available to the construction industry, particular emphasis being placed on mix design and on identifying the merits and limitations of the material.

2 PRODUCTION

The various fibre reinforced mixes were produced using a laboratory power driven pan and paddle mixer. The concrete constituents were mixed for two minutes after which a predetermined quantity of fibres was progressively added via a reciprocating fibre dispenser attached to the mixer. The dispenser ensured that the fibres entered the concrete matrix individually, a requirement which had previously been found to be important if uniform fibre distribution was to be achieved and essential when adding fibres having an aspect ratio greater than 100.

3 WORKABILITY

The workability of conventional structural concretes is normally chosen to suit compaction by vibration. When such mixes are discharged into formwork containing congested reinforcement, they still respond to vibration although the response may be slower than desired. In the case of concretes containing a high concentration of steel fibres, however, it may require careful mix design to achieve sufficient workability to permit compaction by vibration, since badly designed composites may not respond when vibrated.

3.1 Techniques

Whilst the slump test[4] is commonly used to assess the workability of conventional concretes, it is not generally suitable for fibre reinforced concretes because many fibrous mixes respond satisfactorily to vibration even though they have zero slump. As a result, the V–B consistometer test[4] was used for all composites and, in addition, the compacting factor test[4] was compared with the V–B test for mortars. The merit of the V–B test is that it simulates, at least in some respects, the compaction of concrete by vibration in practice.

3.2 Results

A wide range of steel fibres was incorporated at various concentrations into cement paste, mortar, 10 mm concrete and 20 mm concrete mixes. Details of the mixes are given in Table 1, and fibre types are shown in Table 2 and Figure 2.

Table 1 Mix proportions

| Matrix type | Cement OPC | Weight of mix constituents | | | | | | Free water | Total water |
| | | Aggregate (oven dry)* | | | | | | | |
		20–10 mm	10–5 mm	5–2.4 mm	2.4 mm–600 μm	Pass. 600 μm	Total		
Paste	1	–	–	–	–	–	0	0.26	0.26
Mortar	1	–	–	0.34	0.74	1.32	2.40	0.40	0.43
10 mm concrete	1	–	1.36	0.44	0.82	0.78	3.40	0.40	0.48
20 mm concrete	1	1.60	0.88	0.28	0.56	0.68	4.00	0.40	0.47

  * The aggregate was an uncrushed irregular Thames Valley gravel which was presoaked prior to use to allow for absorption.

Typical relationships between workability and fibre content for fibre reinforced mortars containing different types of fibres are shown on Figure 3*, for the V–B test, and Figure 4 for the compacting factor test. From these results it is apparent that the workability of any mix decreases with increase in fibre concentration and fibre aspect ratio.

---

* In this and in subsequent figures, experimental points are omitted for clarity.

Table 2 Fibre types used, also shown in Figure 2

Fibre diameter (mm)	Fibre length (mm)	Surface characteristics	Fibre manufacturer
0.15	5	Brass coated	Steel Cords Ltd
0.15	10	Brass coated	Steel Cords Ltd
0.15	25	Plain round	National Standard Co Ltd
0.15	38	Plain round	National Standard Co Ltd
0.18	5	Brass coated	Steel Cords Ltd
0.18	10	Brass coated	Steel Cords Ltd
0.20	25	Brass coated	Steel Cords Ltd
0.25	20	Plain round	Johnson & Nephew Ltd
0.25	25	Plain round	National Standard Co Ltd
0.25	25	Duoform*	National Standard Co Ltd
0.25	25	Brass coated	N V Bekaert Ltd
0.25	25	Plain round	Tinsley Wire Industries Ltd
0.25	25	Brass coated	Steel Cords Ltd
0.25	30	Brass coated	Steel Cords Ltd
0.25	38	Plain round	National Standard Co Ltd
0.25	38	Plain round	Tinsley Wire Industries Ltd
0.25	50	Plain round	Johnson & Nephew Ltd
0.35	30	Plain round	N V Bekaert Ltd
0.38	12	Duoform*	National Standard Co Ltd
0.38	20	Brass coated	National Standard Co Ltd
0.38	25	Plain round	National Standard Co Ltd
0.38	25	Rusted	National Standard Co Ltd
0.38	25	Duoform*	National Standard Co Ltd
0.38	38	Plain round	National Standard Co Ltd
0.38	38	Duoform*	National Standard Co Ltd
0.50	38	Plain round	National Standard Co Ltd
0.50	38	Brass coated	National Standard Co Ltd
0.50	38	Duoform*	National Standard Co Ltd
0.50	50	Crimped	GKN Ltd

*Duoform is a patented fibre shape.

Although not apparent from Figures 3 and 4, it is worth emphasising that it is not the actual length or the diameter of the included fibres which is important but the ratio of the fibre length/ diameter.

It may therefore be concluded for a given workability that (i) a higher volume fraction of low aspect ratio fibres may be incorporated into a mix, or conversely that (ii) the higher the aspect ratio of the included fibres, the lower will be the volume concentration than can be incorporated in the mix.

It can be seen from Figure 3 that the V–B test identifies a critical fibre content for each fibre aspect ratio beyond which the response to vibration rapidly decreases. This is not so for the compacting factor results shown in Figure 4 and this is regarded as a limitation of the test which was in any case suspect since the mixes all required rodding through the hoppers.

114

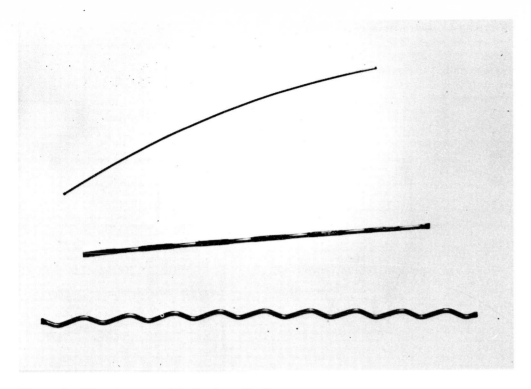

Figure 2   Fibre types used in the investigation

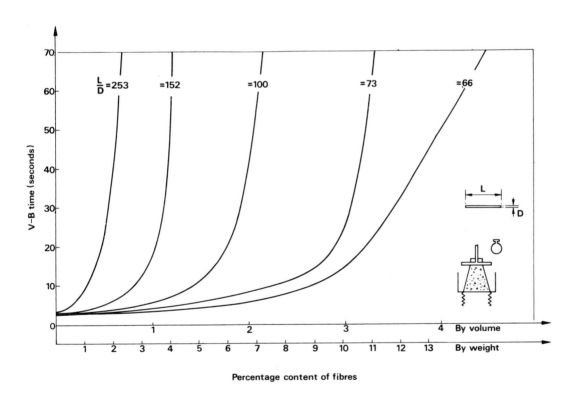

Figure 3   Effect of fibre aspect ratio on V–B time of fibre reinforced mortar

However, as a preliminary guide for work on steel fibre reinforced mortars, a comparison of V–B and compaction factor values is given in Figure 5, further work being necessary to establish whether or not this is applicable to concretes.

Figure 6 shows the relationship between fibre content and V–B time for fibres with an aspect ratio of 100 in matrices ranging from cement paste through to concretes having 20 mm maximum sized aggregate. From this it can be seen that the exponential type relationship established between fibre content and V–B time for mortar (Figure 3) exists for other matrices. Also the fibre content, beyond which the workability of the composite rapidly decreases, becomes less as the size of the coarse aggregate increases. It is also apparent from Figure 6 that the workability characteristics of fibre reinforced paste and mortar are broadly similar, thus indicating that the presence of aggregate particles up to 5 mm size has little influence on the compaction characteristics of fibre reinforced cement paste. Hence it would appear that for a given fibre type and orientation the workability of a mix decreases as the size and quantity of aggregate particles greater than 5 mm increases.

It has been found that a reasonable estimate of the fibre content required to make the concrete effectively unworkable can be obtained from the following equation:

$$PWc_{crit} = 75 \cdot \frac{\pi \cdot SG_f}{SG_c} \cdot \frac{d}{L} \cdot K$$

where PWc_{crit} = critical percentage of fibres, by weight of concrete matrix

SG_f = specific gravity of fibres

SG_c = specific gravity of concrete matrix

$\dfrac{d}{L}$ = inverse of fibre aspect ratio

and K = $\dfrac{Wm}{W_m + W_a}$ in which

W_m = weight of the mortar fraction, ie that part of matrix whose particle size is less than 5 mm,

W_a = weight of the aggregate fraction whose particle size is greater than 5 mm.

In order to ensure, however, that the workability of a composite is sufficient to allow compaction by substantial external vibration it is recommended that the fibre content should not exceed $\frac{3}{4}$ PWc_{crit}.

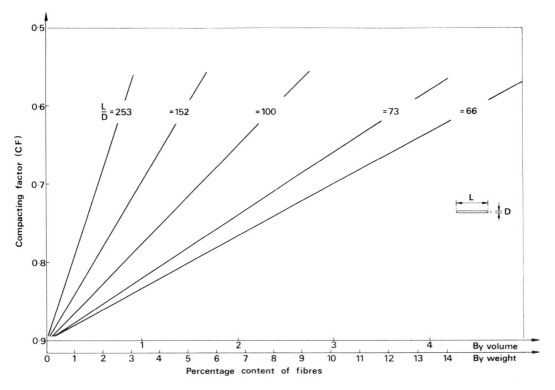

Figure 4 Effect of fibre aspect ratio on compacting factor of fibre reinforced mortars

116

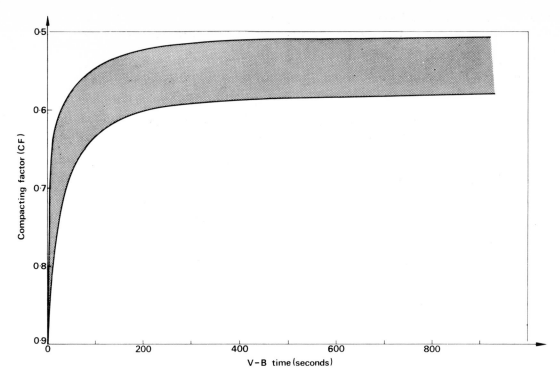

Figure 5   Relationship between compacting factor and V–B time for fibre reinforced mortars

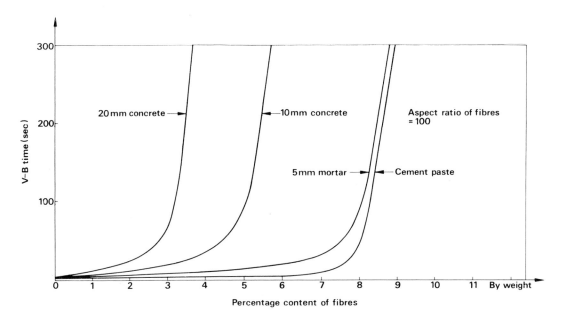

Figure 6   Workability against fibre content for matrices with different maximum aggregate size

4 COMPACTION

In the case of glass fibre reinforced cements, it has been reported [5] that the addition of glass fibres results in considerable air entrapment and, since air reduces the strength of concrete, a study was made of the air content of compacted steel fibre reinforced specimens.

The results of the study revealed that, provided the composite was capable of compaction on a vibrating table, the air content of the matrix within fibre reinforced concretes is no greater than that of the matrix without fibres. It was also found that in the case of fibre reinforced mortars there exists a trend of decreasing air content with increasing fibre content, and this may be due to damping effects of the fibres.

5   MODULUS OF ELASTICITY

From the results of uniaxial tensile stress-strain measurements on 100 mm x 100 mm x 500 mm plain and fibre reinforced specimens, it has been established that including fibres into the various cementitious matrices, shown in Table 1, only marginally increases the elastic modulus of the composite relative to that of the matrix (Table 3). This finding is consistent with the order of increase predicted by applying the laws of mixtures, the volume fraction of steel fibres being insufficient to change greatly the elastic deformation of the matrix.

Table 3   Effect of fibres on tensile modulus of elasticity

Matrix	Volume of fibre reinforcement (%)	Tensile modulus of elasticity (average of 3 specimens) GN/m^2
Cement paste	0 2.70	26.4 28.4
Mortar	0 2.34	33.9 34.8
10 mm concrete	0 1.47	39.7 40.9

Compressive stress-strain measurements on plain and fibre reinforced 10 mm concrete showed similar small increases in modulus, the values in tension and compression being essentially equal.

6   CRACKING AND DUCTILITY

An investigation was undertaken to examine in some detail the cracking and failure behaviour of the material, the main objectives being to determine the effect of steel fibres on the cracking strain of the matrix and on the tensile cracking stress in relation to the 6.9 MN/m^2 claimed for the material by the patent [2].

6.1   Techniques

The onset and progression of cracking was determined on 100 mm x 100 mm x 500 mm specimens tested in flexure [4] and in uniaxial tension. The flexure specimens were instrumented so that continuous recordings could be made at increasing loads of the following parameters:

(i)   Ultrasonic pulse time along the longitudinal axis of the tension zone of specimens. Changes in pulse time were considered to be indicative of cracking

(ii)   Central deflection

(iii)   Tensile strain near the bottom surface

(iv)   Neutral axis position.

The deflection and strain measurements were made using linear variable differential transformers (lvdt) as shown with the ultransonic transducers on a test specimen in Figure 7.

In the case of the direct tension tests, longitudinal strains and pulse times were measured using similar techniques to those used in flexure.

6.2   Results

The results obtained in flexure tests on a typical plain and a typical fibre reinforced specimen are shown in Figure 8, from which the following observations are made:

(a) A change in pulse time occurs at a lower load than changes in slope of either the load-deflection or load-strain curves. Also cracking, as interpreted from the pulse time data, initiates at approximately the same load in both specimens and this was consistently the case throughout the test programme. It is therefore concluded that the presence of fibres does not have a significant influence in elevating the strain at which micro-cracking initiates in the matrix.

118

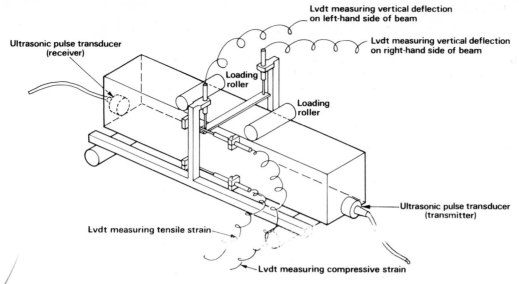

Figure 7 Equipment for detecting cracking under flexural loading

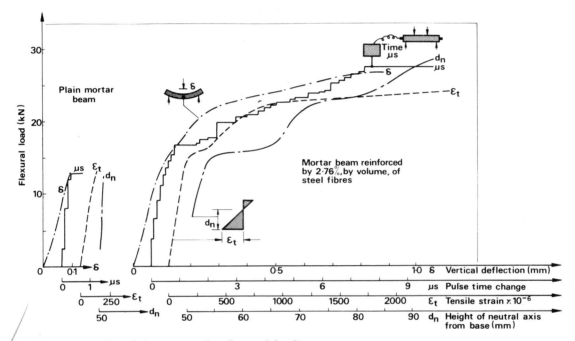

Figure 8 Cracking behaviour under flexural loading

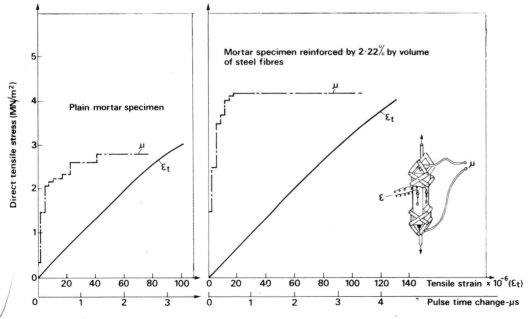

Figure 9 Cracking under direct tensile loading

(b) The plain specimen exhibits the characteristics expected from a semi-brittle material such as concrete in that the load-strain and load-deflection curves remained virtually linear up to failure, the neutral axis position was relatively stable with increasing load and only small changes in pulse time occurred before sudden failure. In the case of the fibre reinforced specimen, however, considerable quasi-plastic behaviour occurs once macro-cracking initiates, in this instance at a load of approximately 15 kN.

One of the most significant features of the fibre reinforced specimens is the progressive movement upwards of the neutral axis from the centre of the specimen as load is increased from 15 kN to failure at about 30 kN. Thus attempts to use the modulus of rupture[4] of fibre reinforced specimens as a measure of the maximum tensile stress at failure will result in a considerable overestimate. This is because the modulus of rupture, as defined in BS 1881[4], assumes that the neutral axis remains at half the depth of the specimen until failure. This is an important finding and one which must be carefully considered when judging the claims made regarding the tensile properties of steel fibre reinforced concrete.

A set of results obtained from the more limited programme of tests in uniaxial tension is shown on Figure 9.

It can be seen that pulse time changes initiated at a stress level less than 2 MN/m^2 for both specimens and in no case were time changes detected in other specimens at stresses greater than 2.6 MN/m^2. This evidence does not support the claims made by the patent[2] that the tensile cracking stress of concrete is elevated to beyond 6.9 MN/m^2 by the incorporation of closely spaced steel fibres.

However, an important point is to consider the techniques and terminology used to define the cracking stress. If only a visual assessment or a load-deflection curve is used then there is no doubt that, in testing small beams in flexure, the load at which cracks are judged to form can be increased by the addition of fibres.

7 STRENGTH

7.1 Influence of fibre orientation

It has been found that under table vibration there is a tendency for the steel fibres to align in planes at right angles to the direction of vibration or gravity. The results of this study have already been published[6] and the main conclusions drawn from the work were as follows:

(a) Steel fibre reinforced concrete or mortar products which are nominally randomly reinforced in three dimensions, can exhibit anisotropic behaviour due to fibre orientation during compaction;

(b) The direction of preferential fibre alignment should be made clear when the properties of steel fibre reinforced composites are quoted;

(c) From the practical point of view of manufacturing steel fibre reinforced cement products, this type of anisotropic behaviour could be put to good effect by arranging the compaction procedure so that the fibres are aligned in the most beneficial direction relative to the stress field. On the other hand, if the effects of vibration on fibre alignment are not fully appreciated, the strengths of steel fibre reinforced concrete products could be much lower than predictions based on laboratory tests using different compaction procedures.

7.2 Flexural[4], uniaxial tensile and torsional strengths

The strengths were determined from 100 mm x 100 mm x 500 mm prisms using the same materials detailed in Tables 1 and 2.

The strengths obtained [3,7] are shown in bands in Figure 10. From this figure it can be seen that the direct tensile and torsional strengths of concretes are only marginally increased. The flexural strengths, however, are considerably increased, the plain concrete strength being doubled by the addition of certain fibre types at 2 per cent by volume. Thus it may be concluded that the addition of steel fibres to concrete enables small flexural members to sustain considerably increased loading whilst, at the same time, the actual tensile strength of the material is only marginally increased.

It has been shown[3] that these marginal increases in tensile strength can be adequately predicted using the conventional theory of mixtures, ie reinforced concrete theory, when efficiency factors for the fibre reinforcement are introduced to allow for fibre orientation and to take account of bond strength.

120

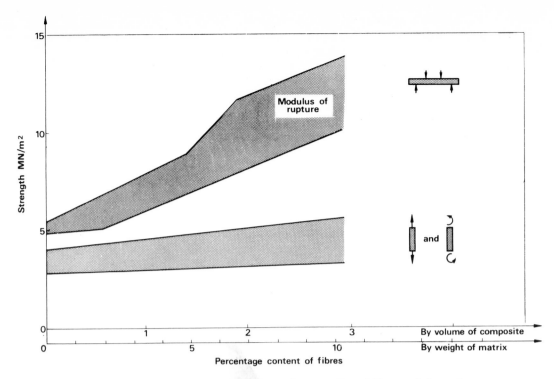

Figure 10   Flexural, direct tensile and torsional strengths of fibre reinforced
mortar and concrete

The theoretical prediction of increased tensile strength with decreasing fibre spacing by
Romualdi and Batson[1] is shown on Figure 11. The experimental results from this present
investigation and those of Shah and Rangan[8] and of Johnston and Coleman[9] are also shown on
Figure 11 from which it can be seen that for a constant volume of steel the measured tensile
strengths only marginally increase with decreasing fibre spacing when compared with the large
increases predicted theoretically[1]. Thus the theoretical fibre spacing concept does not in reality
predict the cracking strength of fibre reinforced concretes and therefore some of the claims
made in the patents for steel fibre reinforced concretes have not been substantiated by this investigation. The shortcomings of this aspect of the claims relate principally to a lack of
understanding of the major part played by the method of test in determining the tensile strength
of concrete.

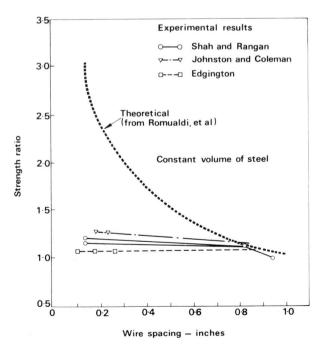

Figure 11   Effect of spacing of reinforcement on
cracking strength of concrete

The inclusion of fibres having different aspect ratios revealed that for a constant volume of steel the loads carried by flexural specimens increased as the aspect ratio of the fibres increased and this is attributed to the increased effective bond length. It has been shown in Section 3, however, that for a constant volume of fibres, the workability of the composite decreases as the aspect ratio of the fibres increases. In design, therefore, it is necessary to optimise between considerations of strength and workability, increasing one at the cost of the other. Figure 12 illustrates, for a mortar matrix, the way in which aspect ratio and fibre content are interrelated to achieve the same load carried by a beam expressed as modulus of rupture.

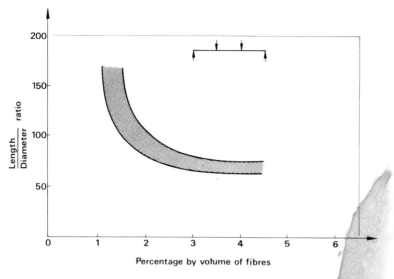

Figure 12   Fibre volume to achieve a modulus of rupture of 9 MN/m^2 in mortar

Although the detailed results show that the modulus of rupture of specimens containing crimped or indented fibres was slightly higher than those containing plain round wire at similar fibre concentrations and aspect ratios, no single fibre type proved to be significantly better than the others at all concentrations for improving the tensile or flexural strengths.

7.3 Compressive strength

Only small increases in the uniaxial compressive strength of mortar and concrete prisms and cylinders were achieved by the addition of steel fibres. The small increases in strength could have been more cheaply achieved by decreasing the water/cement ratio although the reinforced specimens have the merit of pronounced ductility.

7.4 Effect of age

It has been established from tests carried out at specimen ages ranging from 7 to 112 days that the strength of steel fibre reinforced concrete increases at a rate similar to that of unreinforced concrete.

8 MECHANISM OF FIBRE STRENGTHENING IN FLEXURE

It has been stated in Section 7 that the maximum flexural load sustained by a concrete or mortar beam may be considerably increased by the inclusion of steel fibres whilst there is only a marginal increase in the uniaxial tensile strength of the material. It is suggested that the increased load-carrying capacity is due to the partially plastic stress blocks developed within the tensile zone of fibre reinforced beams, as compared with the predominantly linear elastic stress blocks thought to exist within unreinforced beams.

8.1 Hypothesis

Consider a fibre reinforced concrete beam subjected to an increasing load $(P + \Delta P)$ as shown in Figure 13a. As the tensile strain increases, cracks are formed but, unlike plain concrete, a

122

proportion of the load is maintained across the crack by those fibres spanning the crack and hence equilibrium is maintained. Due to the formation of these cracks the measured tensile strains are increased and hence the neutral axis moves upwards to some new value. When further load is applied to the beam, the measured tensile strains increase at a greater rate than the compressive strains, see Figure 13b, and the values, d_n', increase until there is no simple relationship between the measured strain and the apparent stress sustained across the crack. The stress block in the tensile zone will then probably be represented by Figure 13c with a limit of 13d as the maximum tensile area which can be developed.

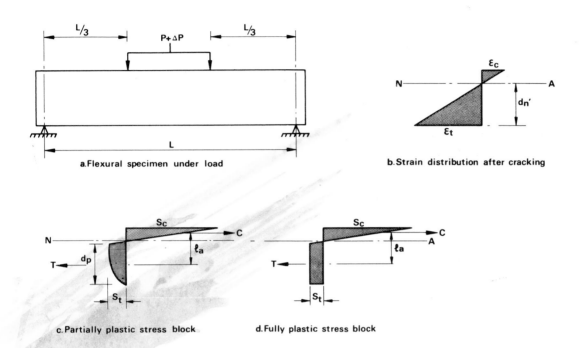

a. Flexural specimen under load

b. Strain distribution after cracking

c. Partially plastic stress block

d. Fully plastic stress block

Figure 13 Suggested mechanism of fibre strengthening in flexure

8.2 Procedure adopted to check hypothesis

The compressive and tensile strains, and hence the neutral axis position, were measured up to failure for a wide range of plain and fibre reinforced specimens. The maximum tensile strength of each composite was known from the strength investigation.

A triangular stress distribution in the compressive zone of the beams was assumed because in general the maximum measured compressive strains were less than the strain at which the material becomes significantly inelastic.

Using values obtained from the tests the following were calculated at 95 per cent of the ultimate load.

(a) The compressive force C

Where $C = \dfrac{\epsilon_c \times E \times b \times (d - d_n)}{2}$

in which ϵ_c = compressive strain

E = modulus of elasticity

b = breadth of beam

d = depth of beam

d_n = height of neutral axis from tensile face.

(b) From various assumed shapes of the tensile stress block, ie between partially plastic (Figure 13c) and fully plastic (Figure 13d)

123

(i)   the maximum tensile stress, (St), by equating T = C

(ii)   the lever arm (la)

(iii)   the moment of resistance = la x T

(iv)   the theoretical sustained flexural load (P_{th}) by equating moment of resistance to bending moment, from which $P_{th} = \dfrac{6 \times la \cdot T}{L}$

The derived values of P_{th} and St were then compared with the measured values to identify a shape of stress block which would accurately predict the specimen failure load when the maximum tensile stress, St, was within the range determined from the direct tension tests. In addition to the assumptions made regarding the shape of the stress block, some error may have been introduced in the strain measurements due to the size of the lvdt supports but the results given in Table 4 suggest that reasonable agreement is obtained between predicted and observed behaviour. Of the 100 specimens tested, the failure load was predicted in each case to within an accuracy of ±20 per cent. It is therefore concluded that the improved load-carrying capacity of steel fibre reinforced beams is due to the formation of plastic or partially plastic tensile stress blocks and not to an increase in the tensile strength of the composite.

Table 4 Comparison of theoretical and experimental failure loads

Matrix type	Percentage of fibres by volume	Theoretical values		Experimental results		
		$0.95P_{th}$ (kN)	St (MN/m^2)	$0.95P_{actual}$ (kN)	Range of measured direct tensile strength (MN/m^2)	
					minimum	maximum
Cement paste	0.82	17.0	4.96	18.1	4.77	5.15
	1.50	18.2	5.44	18.7	4.54	5.58
	2.70	19.9	5.33	19.4	5.03	5.51
	3.61	25.2	5.56	25.6	5.02	6.27
Mortar	0	11.7	3.57	12.1	3.13	4.00
	1.12	13.1	3.95	14.8	3.91	4.04
	1.81	25.9	4.84	25.5	4.50	4.92
	2.76	30.6	5.21	28.6	5.00	5.36
10 mm concrete	0	10.5	3.21	10.3	2.97	3.55
	1.18	17.6	4.05	17.7	3.87	4.14
	1.75	20.3	4.18	20.5	3.76	4.43
20 mm concrete	0.60	11.9	3.15	11.7	2.89	3.21
	1.19	15.6	3.16	15.9	2.61	3.21

It should be emphasised that although the areas and shapes of the calculated tensile stress blocks may be accurate for the purpose of calculating the moment of resistance of the beams, the tensile stresses are not real quantities. This is because the 'real' quantities are the forces in the individual fibres spanning cracks and these are effectively integrated, averaged and divided by the beam cross-sectional area to give a quantity which is convenient for engineering design, known as the average tensile stress in the composite. This is the same convenient quantity as is measured in a direct tensile test after matrix cracking and must not be confused with the modulus of rupture.

9 IMPACT

The impact toughness of various fibre reinforced composites was assessed using 100 mm x 100 mm x 500 mm specimens. A pendulum type impact machine was modified as shown in Figure 14 so that an estimate could be made of the energy required to displace and rotate the fractured specimen halves.

The results obtained for mortar and for 10 mm and 20 mm maximum sized concretes are shown on Figure 15. It is clear that the impact toughness of concrete is considerably increased by incorporating steel fibres, the improvements being especially favourable with the 0.50 mm dia x 50 mm high tensile crimped fibre, but further work is required to establish whether this is due to the shape or the strength of this type of fibre.

124

Figure 14 Impact machine

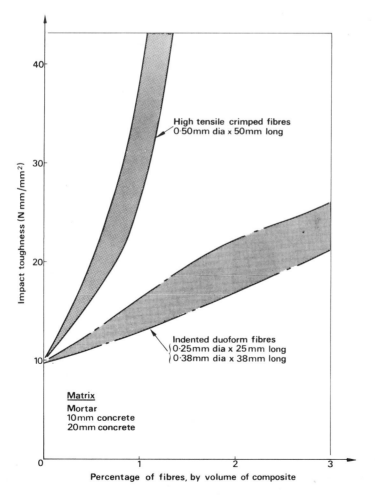

Figure 15 Impact toughness of fibre reinforced
mortar and concrete

10 TIME-DEPENDENT PROPERTIES

10.1 Creep

From the results of compressive creep tests carried out over a loading period of 12 months it has been found that the addition of steel fibres in concrete does not reduce the creep strains of the composite. This behaviour is consistent with the low volume concentration of fibres when compared with an aggregate volume of approximately 70 per cent.

10.2 Shrinkage

The shrinkage of concrete over a period of 3 months on specimens subjected to various curing environments was unaffected by the presence of steel fibres. This again is as expected for the same reasons given for creep.

10.3 Durability

The weathering of plain and fibre reinforced normal and lightweight aggregate concretes was observed over a period of 3 years. For this study, cylindrical specimens were exposed at BRE, Garston, and also to aggressive environments on Department of the Environment exposure sites at Hurst Castle in the Solent, and at Beckton gas works, London. Apart from rust staining on the outer faces, the specimens exhibited no significant deterioration over the period of exposure, the rate of carbonation being the same for the plain and for the fibre reinforced specimens. The depth of penetration of carbonation was greater for the lightweight aggregate concretes.

The specimens used however were in an uncracked condition and further work is in progress to judge the long-term structural integrity of specimens containing cracks.

11 APPLICATIONS AND ECONOMICS

Having identified the stress systems for which concretes may be improved by the addition of steel fibres, it is now possible to consider suitable applications. The most beneficial characteristics of fibre reinforced systems are those of increased flexural capacity, toughness, post-failure ductility and crack control. The following are applications referred to in published papers:

> Airfield and highway pavements both for new construction and as overlays, bridge nosings and bridge decks, loading bays, heavy duty floors and chutes; tunnel linings, machine bases, security safes and strong rooms; thin precast components subjected to flexural or impact loading such as pile shells, paving slabs, fence posts, steps, manhole covers, duct covers and cast iron replacements; domes, shells, concrete boats and marine structures; regions of high shear stress such as prestressed, post-tensioned concrete end blocks; structures requiring resistance to thermal shock such as refractory linings, and fire-resistant coatings for beams and columns; more exotic applications such as explosives stores, pads for vertical take-off aircraft and tank turning pads.

The most advantageous outlets are still rather uncertain but the authors' experiences suggest that the main practical applications will be in paving, precast components and in those situations where toughness and post-failure ductility are important. The rate of progress will depend on economic considerations and may be influenced by future work in which the durability of cracked sections is examined.

At the current price of 25 to 30p/kg for steel fibres, the addition of 1 per cent by volume to the concrete more than trebles the material costs. At first sight this increase seems prohibitive but when fabrication and manufacturing costs are taken into account the materials costs represent only a fraction of the total cost. Furthermore, if conventional reinforcement can thereby be reduced or eliminated, the savings in cost of detailing, receiving, cutting, bending, and fixing conventional reinforcement may offset the increased materials cost.

12 CONCLUSIONS

Mixing and fibre distribution

1 A mixer with a power-driven pan and a power-driven paddle, which rotates in the same direction as the pan, provides a good mixing action for the production of steel fibre reinforced concrete.

2 The sequence in which the mix constituents are added to the mixer has no apparent influence on the resultant degree of fibre dispersion.

3 In order to ensure good fibre distribution, the fibres should reach the concrete individually and be immediately removed from the point of entry by the mixing action. This may be readily achieved by passing the fibres through a mechanically operated sieve into the type of mixer described in 1 above.

4 Fibre dispersion is more easily achieved when incorporating fibres of a low aspect ratio. As a result, higher volume fractions of wire can be used in a given matrix when the aspect ratio is low.

5 Uniform dispersion of a given fibre type within a concrete matrix becomes more difficult to achieve as the proportion of aggregate particles greater than 5 mm increases.

Workability and compaction

6 In general, the slump test provides very little indication of either the workability or the ease with which fibre reinforced concrete can be compacted.

7 The V–B test is the best of the 3 standard workability tests for assessing the behaviour of fresh fibre reinforced concrete subjected to compaction by vibration.

8 The workability of a composite is decreased as the fibre content is increased and there is a critical fibre volume above which the rate of decrease in workability is very rapid.

9 The most important single fibre characteristic which influences workability is the aspect ratio.

10 When the fibre concentration is held constant then the workability of a composite is decreased as the aspect ratio of the included fibres is increased.

11 When the fibre concentration and aspect ratio are held constant then the workability of the composite is decreased as the ratio:

$$\frac{\text{volume of cement paste} + \text{aggregate particles less than 5 mm in size}}{\text{total volume of the matrix}}$$

decreases.

Strength

12 The increase in the direct tensile, torsional and compressive strengths of fibre reinforced concretes, when compared with their unreinforced counterparts, are relatively small even at a fibre concentration of up to 5 per cent by volume. Hence there is likely to be little practical merit in including short random steel fibres in concrete to increase any of these strengths.

13 Significant increases in the modulus of rupture of fibre reinforced concretes may be achieved when the maximum size of the aggregate particles is not greater than 10 mm. These increases can exceed 100 per cent when 2 per cent by volume of certain fibre types are used.

Cracking

14 The cracking of all direct tensile fibre reinforced specimens initiated at a tensile stress less than 2.6 MN/m^2, this being approximately 1/3 of the value claimed in the Patent[2].

15 The onset of micro-cracking within cementitious matrices subjected to increasing flexural load is apparently unaffected by the presence of steel fibres.

16 The flexural load required for crack propagation is increased as the fibre content increases.

Mechanism of strengthening in direct tension

17 The theory of fibre strengthening, based on fibre spacing[1], grossly overestimates the true direct tensile strength of such composites.

18 A reinforcing theory, based upon the laws of mixtures, enables satisfactory prediction to be made of the direct tensile strength of fibre reinforced concretes. It may, therefore, be concluded that the direct tensile behaviour of fibre reinforced concrete characterises the performance of conventional reinforced concrete in which the reinforcing bars are inefficiently orientated, with respect to the direction of applied stress, and poorly bonded to the concrete matrix.

Mechanism of strengthening in flexure

19 The large increases in the load–carrying capacity of small fibre reinforced concrete beams is due to the formation of plastic or partially plastic stress blocks within the tensile zones of such beams, as a result of the forces maintained by the fibres after matrix cracking. Attempts to interpret the increases in modulus of rupture as being indicative of increased material strength will result in a considerable overestimate of the true tensile strength of the material.

Toughness under impact loading

20 Of the four fibre types investigated, the 0.50 mm diameter x 50 mm long high tensile crimped fibre proved to be the most beneficial at improving the impact toughness of the cementitious matrices. Increases in impact toughness of more than 400 per cent, at less than $1\frac{3}{4}$ per cent by volume, were measured with this fibre.

Dimensional changes

21 The addition of steel fibres to concrete at volume fractions of up to 3 per cent provides only marginal increases in the elastic moduli.

22 The shrinkage of mortar and the creep deformations of gravel aggregate concrete are not significantly reduced by the inclusion of 2 per cent by volume of steel fibres.

ACKNOWLEDGEMENTS

The authors wish to thank the Department of the Environment for financing the project, Mr F J Grimer of the Building Research Establishment for his useful guidance and the laboratory staff of the Construction Materials Research Group at the University of Surrey for their willing help at all times.

13 REFERENCES

1 Romualdi, J P and Batson, G B. Mechanics of crack arrest in concrete. Proceedings of the American Society of Civil Engineers, Vol 89, No EM3, June 1963, pp 147-168.

2 Battelle Development Corporation. Concrete and steel material. British Patent No 1068163, December 1963.

3 Edgington, J. Steel fibre reinforced concrete. Research report submitted to the Department of the Environment, January 1974. Also available as PhD thesis, University of Surrey, 1974.

4 British Standards Institution. BS 1881:1970: Methods of testing concrete.

5 Grimer, F J and Ali, M A. The strength of cements reinforced with glass fibres. Magazine of Concrete Research, Vol 21, No 66, March 1969, pp 23-30.

6 Edgington, J and Hannant, D J. Steel fibre reinforced concrete. The effect on fibre orientation of compaction by vibration. Matériaux et Construction, Vol 5, No 25, 1972, pp 41-44.

7 Edgington, J. Steel fibre reinforced concrete. Intermediate report submitted to the Department of the Environment for the period ending 1st March 1972.

8 Shah, S P and Rangan, B V. Effects of reinforcement on ductility of concrete. Proceedings of the American Society of Civil Engineers, Journal of the Structural Division, June 1970, pp 1167-1184.

9 Johnston, C D and Coleman, R A. Strength and deformation of steel fibre reinforced mortar in uniaxial tension. To be published in the Journal of the American Concrete Institute, 1974.

Fibrous composites as alternative materials

New fibrous composites as alternatives to timber (CP 66/74)

D.F. Cornelius and J.F. Ryder

INTRODUCTION

Timber is a traditional material of construction and about 8 million m^3 of it are used each year by the building and construction industry. Approximately 90 per cent of this is imported and this represents a charge of about £300M a year on our balance of payments. In addition the price of timber has almost doubled over the past couple of years, so there are obvious economic benefits to be obtained by improving the efficiency of timber usage and developing substitutes for timber. A significant programme of research has therefore been undertaken by the Building Research Establishment, both at the Princes Risborough Laboratory and the Building Research Station. That part of it concerned with developing materials capable of replacing timber involves economic and design studies at PRL, while the development of special types of fibre composite materials and components made from them is being studied at BRS; this latter aspect is described in this paper.

Recent developments of new fibrous composite materials and of methods of making a wide variety of components from them now offer the prospect of replacing a substantial proportion of timber by the new materials, some of which can be made entirely from indigenous raw materials, although it is recognised that timber has advantages in being a renewable resource which requires very little energy to produce and prepare for use.

There are two possible approaches to the problem of replacing timber by a new composite material. The first method is to develop and modify the new material so that as far as possible its essential properties are similar to those of timber. The new material could then be used as a direct replacement for timber in the forms in which it is now used.

The alternative approach is to take a particular timber component or structural element, consider its various functions and any relevant performance requirements and design an alternative component to be made from the new composite material. This design will be based on the known properties of the material, and its method of fabrication. The new component need not be of the same shape as the original timber component, provided that it satisfactorily performs the same functions and satisfies the performance requirements.

REPLACEMENT OF TIMBER MATERIAL

What are the properties of timber that until comparatively recently in the history of man's building activities were not available in other materials? Timber is a natural fibrous composite with a high strength to weight ratio. The fibres are parallel to each other and to the axis of the trunk or branch, and the material can be readily cut to size or worked to shape. As a structural material, these properties are most effectively employed when the timber is used, for example, as a beam so that the tensile strength of the uniaxial cellulose fibres is fully utilised. This uniaxial array of the fibres is however a disadvantage when wood is used in sheet form, so for some purposes this natural orientation of the fibres is altered by lamination, as in plywood, to a two-dimensional or planar orientation or to a random three-dimensional array as in chipboard. In such ways it is possible to produce low density, high strength structural materials from timber.

The basic approach to developing a substitute material is to combine the properties of fibre reinforcement with an appropriate matrix to give the desired strength, modulus and density characteristics at an economic cost based on the long-term performance of the system. Most of the work to date has centred on glass fibre reinforced inorganic matrices as these appeared more promising, either technically or economically, than other fibre reinforcement such as steel, carbon, polypropylene etc.

131

Organic matrices

Plastic-based materials have been considered as possible substitutes for timber, but until recently their high cost limited their usefulness for this purpose and they have less satisfactory fire characteristics than inorganic materials. Even so they have significant potential and three distinct types of plastic material have been used: solid plastics, foamed plastics and glass fibre reinforced plastics.

Whilst it is not strictly within the ambit of this paper to consider non-fibrous plastics materials as timber substitutes, it is worth recording briefly their use. Solid plastics can replace timber in applications such as window frames and weatherboarding. The advantages of low maintenance costs and self decoration are obvious and examples are shown in Table 1, but these are offset by limitations such as lack of stiffness and proneness to thermal movement.

Table 1 Cost in use comparison of plastics alternatives

Material	Cost over 60 years $(£/m^2)$
Windows	
Softwood, dip impregnated and painted	17
Steel, galvanised and painted	15.5
Glass fibre reinforced polyester	19.5
Pvc encapsulated timber	18.5
Shiplap weatherboarding	
Wood, primed and painted	4.8
Pvc	3.5
Plastics coated steel	3.7

Recent advances in foaming techniques for plastics reduce significantly the cost per unit volume of the plastic material, and the process of extrusion foaming produces material with a lightweight foam core and a solid skin giving a box-girder shape which is efficient mechanically. With their low density (comparable to that of timber) and economic competitiveness these cellular plastic extrusions become attractive as substitutes for timber in specific applications.

Glass fibre reinforced plastics have, of course, been used in the form of roofing sheet for many years and more recently as cladding panels. Glass fibre reinforced thermoset plastics (eg 20-50 per cent glass to give desired strength/density properties) have full structural capabilities unattainable by any other plastics material and such materials can substitute for timber in structural applications such as roof spans and wall and roof elements but are not used much in this way at present. Although this material is more expensive than traditional materials it can be assembled and dismantled readily and is suited for uses such as formwork.

In general, however, plastics materials are used mainly where appearance or low density is important rather than in structural applications because of their low fire reistance.

Inorganic matrices

Where density is less important there are other possible replacement materials, particularly those based on inorganic matrices such as plaster and cement. The recognised limitations of these materials (low tensile strength and low impact strength) have been successfully overcome by the incorporation of fibrous reinforcement and glass fibres in particular have given good results.

Gypsum can be reinforced by E-glass fibre without difficulty but cement requires alkali resistant glass fibre for its reinforcement; this has been invented at BRE and manufactured and developed by Pilkington Brothers Ltd (who have the exclusive NRDC licence so to do) under the trade name Cem-FIL[1,2]. The strength characteristics of these composites (glass fibre reinforced gypsum, grg, and glass fibre reinforced cement, grc) approach those of sheet timber, but they have higher densities and possibly fixing problems. However, such materials have considerable potential for moulding as floor, wall or roof units and the orientation of the fibres can be controlled by the method of manufacture to give reinforcement where it is needed. Thus incorporating fibres by means of the spray/suction method gives a two-dimensional array of fibres and planar reinforcement; incorporation of fibres by pre-mix method gives a random three-dimensional array and continuous fibres can be added if required. The cost and performance of components made by such methods are described later in this paper.

It is possible to modify the various constituents of the fibrous composite systems in order to obtain specific properties. Thus the adequate durability obtained with grc by the use of alkali resistant glass can be further improved if the matrix is modified by, for example, incorporating pulverised fuel ash. With gypsum plaster there are no durability problems but the composite loses up to 50 per cent of its strength when wetted, although this is fully recovered when the material dries. It is therefore appropriate to base designs on the wet strength of the composite. However, a recent development in this area suggests that this limitation can be overcome at a price.

Most of the work to date has been carried out using glass fibres but polypropylene fibres have been incorporated also. Their low modulus prevents any contribution to the stiffness and strength of the composite but they greatly increase the work of fracture and hence the impact strength of the material.

The glass fibre reinforced cements and plasters thus produced have strength characteristics approaching those for timber (Figures 1 to 3) but their densities are too high so air entrainment and lightweight aggregates have been used to reduce their densities. The most attractive

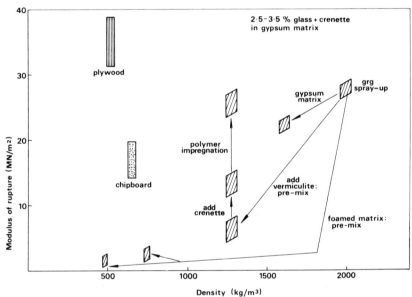

Figure 1 General approach to development of fibrous composites

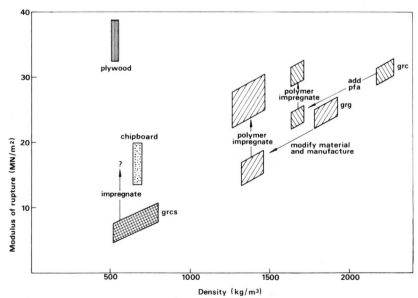

Figure 2 Modulus of rupture/density relations for various fibrous composites; grcs = glass fibre reinforced calcium silicate, pfa = pulverised fuel ash

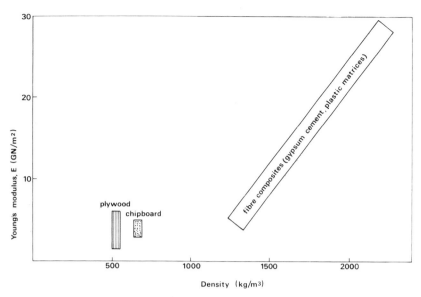

Figure 3 Young's modulus/density relations for fibrous composites

material for this purpose is vermiculite as its soft and deformable nature allows a relatively large volume fraction of fibre to be incorporated even at high 'aggregate' contents. Lower density composites have thus been produced but with correspondingly lower strengths (Figure 1).

Attempts to improve further the strength, toughness and workability of the composites have been made by incorporating polymer emulsions in the composite. Although some were moisture sensitive and unsatisfactory others were beneficial in giving increases in modulus of rupture and impact energy; they were also useful in reducing density due to the air that they entrained.

The greatest improvement in mechanical properties has been obtained by impregnating the fibrous composites with monomers followed by thermal polymerisation (polymer impregnation). In this way the loss in strength due to the incorporation of entrained air and the use of lightweight aggregates has been fully compensated and fibrous composites having densities or strengths approaching those of sheet timber are now being obtained, although Young's moduli are somewhat different (Figure 3).

There is still further potential for development of these composite materials, for example by the use of mixed fibres and by optimising fully the design of fibres. Recent work on this at BRE shows that the strength properties of composites can be improved by appropriate design of the sliver, as shown in Table 2.

Table 2 Relation between sliver design and composite properties

Composite property	Effect of increasing fibre		
	diameter	length	number of filaments per strand
Tensile strength	–	+	–
Modulus of rupture	–	+	–
Impact strength	+	+	–
Young's modulus	0	0	0
Creep and fatigue	–	0	

+ increase in property   – decrease in property   0 no change

Performance characteristics of fibre reinforced inorganic matrices

The range of composite materials produced have strength or density characteristics similar to those of plywood and chipboard. For the non-impregnated boards there is a strong correlation between strength and density. There appears to be no such correlation between impact strength and density, and very high impact energies have been recorded for very low density composite materials, and in this respect composite materials can be produced which are superior to plywood and chipboard.

Most of the composite boards produced based on inorganic matrices can be easily sawn, chiselled, drilled, nailed and screwed and in this respect they may be considered as suitable substitutes for timber, but they are less satisfactory from the point of view of screw pull resistance which is only about one-half of that measured for timber sheet materials of similar density.

The non-impregnated composite materials developed are similar to various timber sheet materials in modulus of rupture or Young's modulus, but are generally of higher density. This may be the premium that has to be paid with materials of this type in order to obtain improved fire and rot resistance compared with that of timber based materials.

The new generation of fibrous composites containing lightweight aggregates and impregnated with polymers that have been developed with strength and density characteristics approaching those of timber sheet material are still under development. Their general performance so far suggests that it will be technically feasible to produce a fibrous composite having essential properties similar to those of some timber materials, but the cost may be high.

Some of the fibrous composites are cheaper than timber, others are not; but it is not relevant to make this type of comparison as all experience to date suggests that they will be used to produce components giving a performance in use similar to timber components, but with designs which may differ significantly from the traditional design of timber components. For this reason it is only useful to compare the total costs (initial plus maintenance) of such components with the timber component giving equivalent performance in use and examples of this are given later in this paper.

REPLACEMENT OF TIMBER COMPONENTS

The difficulties of combining high strength and low density in the same material to replace timber can be avoided by the other approach to the problem, namely by developing components that will perform the same functions as the existing timber components. For this approach, the denser but high strength composites offer a number of advantages. Perhaps the most important of these is that the materials can be moulded, without wastage, to various shapes including hollow sections, so that the problem of weight can be overcome without loss in strength. Also, it is possible to orient the fibres in preferred directions and to control their distribution in the matrix. This ability to control the fibre direction may be compared with the necessity for the early carpenters and shipwrights to select naturally curved or forked branches to obtain timber with the fibres oriented to suit a structural need.

These advantages are most clearly and simply demonstrated by the recent development by BRS of a grc fencepost. Although this is intended to replace reinforced concrete posts rather than timber posts, it will be apparent that the principle could be extended to grc telegraph poles or other replacements for timber[3].

Figure 4 Grc fenceposts

The prototype posts, shown in Figure 4, are tubular, with a wall thickness of 12 mm and an internal diameter of 100 mm tapering to 80 mm over a length of 1 m. They were made on a rotating suction mandrel from a pre-mix of cement slurry and Cem-FIL roving chopped to 10 mm lengths. The proportion of glass fibre in this pre-mix was 4.5 per cent of the weight of dry cement. The thickness of the layer of dewatered mix that built up on the mandrel was controlled by a hinged doctor blade. Continuous lengths of longitudinal roving could also be incorporated within the layer, so that both the orientation and the position of this additional fibre provided the most effective reinforcement of the post when this was subjected to bending stresses.

The load-deflection curves in Figure 5 show that an addition of this longitudinal roving corresponding to 3 per cent of the final weight of the post, increases the load at the elastic limit from 4 kN to 5 kN, and the ultimate failing load from 5.5 kN to 15 kN. These values can be compared with the load of 6.75 kN at which the first cracks in the reinforced concrete post were observed, which is the effective failing load for this type of post.

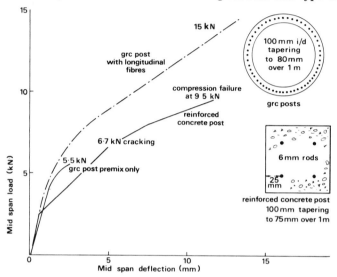

Figure 5 Transverse tests on fenceposts (on 900 mm span)

The deflection of the grc posts is only about half that of the concrete posts, yet they weigh only one-third as much. An average delivered price for a grc post containing a total of 5 per cent of Cem-FIL fibre is broadly comparable with that for a reinforced concrete post of similar dimensions.

The continuous roving reinforcement could readily be incorporated as a helical winding if this rotating mandrel process were to be used to make grc pipes of small to medium diameter.

Housing components

The component approach to timber substitution will obviously be most effective if it is directed towards those components that require the largest amounts of timber. The average house, of traditional construction and having a floor area of 80 m^2, incorporates 7.6 m^3 of timber. Table 3 shows how the various parts of the house contribute to this total. The roof and the suspended floor together account for almost 60 per cent of it, and the timber components used in their construction must therefore be primary targets for replacement.

A glass fibre reinforced gypsum plaster structural floor that could replace the joists, boards and ceiling in a house, and that satisfied the relevant performance requirements, was in fact the first fibre composite component to be developed by BRS, and has been described in detail[4]. Essentially it consisted of two 11 mm thick sheets of spray/suction grg joined by webs of the same material to form a box section 130 mm deep, weighing 50 kg/m^2. When tested on a span of 3.66 m, the uniformly distributed load at the elastic limit was 7.6 kN/m^2, which is five times the requirement for floors of two-storey housing. The load at failure was 16.2 kN/m^2. The average airborne sound reduction index was 28 dB for the bare floor, and 30 dB when it was covered with thermoplastic tiles. The comparable figure for a timber joist and boarded floor, with a ceiling of plasterboard with one coat of plaster is 32dB. The lower figure for the grg floor, despite its greater weight, may be explained by its greater rigidity, which decreases the amount of sound energy absorbed by the floor itself.

More recently, an experimental GRC roof component, in effect a purlin tile, has been developed and tested by BRS. It is intended to span between gable walls with possibly intermediate support from a structural partition or truss, and to replace not only the timber trusses, purlins and battens in a traditional pitched roof, but also the tiles and sarking. However in view of the

Table 3 Timber usage of the average house of traditional construction and 80 m^2 floor area

Area of use	Volume (m^3)		April 1974 prices	
	Range	Average	Price (£/m^3)	Cost per house (£)
Roof				
Trusses	1.45 – 2.20	1.80	65	117
Battens		0.5	65	33
First floor				
Joists	1.00 – 1.80	1.40	65	91
Boards	0.59 – 1.07	0.86	80	69
Window surrounds	0 – 0.35	0.35	100	35
Door frames	0.30	0.30	100	30
Stairs	0.26	0.26	110	30
Partitions	0.3 – 2.0	1.0	65	65
Shelves, cupboards, etc	1.10	1.10		110
Total		7.6		580

unsuitability, at present, of GRC for any structural purpose where failure could result in loss of life or in injury, such structural use must need await the results of the continuing research programme on the long term durability of this material and of the effects of modifications to improve it. It should be noted, however, that the box section shape of this purlin tile affords considerable protection from the weather to the lower (tensile) face so that this would be subjected only to dry conditions and moderate temperatures. The effect of such protection together with the use of additional reinforcement in the tensile face is being examined to determine whether the component retains more than adequate strength throughout its required life.

This component is made by folding 9 mm thick GRC sheet made by the spray suction process to the shape shown in Figure 7 and uses 5 per cent of 33 mm Cem-FIL roving having a planar orientation – additional longitudinal roving can be sandwiched at the tensile face at the box section as shown for unit R in Figure 7.

The load deflection curves in Figure 7, for flexural tests on these units, loaded at the third points on a span of 3.66 m, show that this additional reinforcement in unit R, which was equi-

Figure 6 Demonstration roof of grc purlin tiles

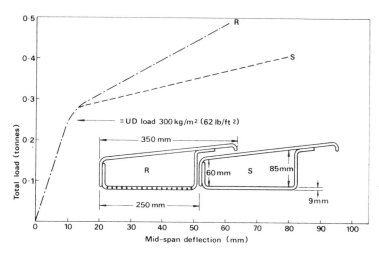

Figure 7 Transverse test on grc purlin tiles (third point loading on 3.66 span)

valent to only 0.5 per cent of the final weight, had no effect on the load at the elastic limit but did decrease the subsequent deflection. The extent of this deflection, for these prototype units, prevented these tests being continued to ultimate failure.

In the first tests on a 3.66 m span, the 0.24 tonne load at the elastic limit is equivalent to a uniformly distributed load of 3 kN/m^2 (62 lbf/ft^2) perpendicular to the roof surface. On this span therefore, the units easily satisfy the strength requirement of the British Standard Code of Basic Data for the Design of Buildings. For pitched roofs, the most severe requirements of this code are for slopes between 10° and 30°, and are that the imposed load to be allowed for is 0.75 kN/m^2 (15.7 lbf/ft^2) measured on plan, or a vertical load for 0.7 kN (202 lbf) concentrated on a square with a 300 mm side. For spans much greater than 3.66 m it may be necessary to increase the depth of the box section, or to provide some intermediate support.

The cost of the grc purlin tiles, delivered on site, has been estimated as £2 per metre length. The cost data in Table 4, calculated on this basis, show that this type of roof should be similar in cost to normal tiled roofs. However, the unobstructed roof space and the flat undersurface provided by the purlin tiles allows effective use to be made of the attic space. The box section can be filled with insulating foam or quilt to provide an acceptable U value, whilst the units can readily be adapted to a Mansard roof construction to provide more habitable space at little extra cost.

Table 4 Comparison between roof of grc purlin tiles, and traditional roofs

Data for house of typical cross wall design, 5 m between cross walls and 8.5 m front to rear. Roof area 48 m^2, pitch 30°.

	Cost (£)	Price (£/m^2)	Weight (kg/m^2)
Grc purlin tile roof			
Grc units, 40 at £10	400		
Sealing strips, bolts, etc	20		
Fit to structure, seal and bolt	60		
	480	10	68 (total)
Roof of single lap concrete tiles			
Roof timber and construction 1.97 m^3 at £154/m^3	303		
Tiles, felt and battens, fitted 48 m^2 at £2.51/m^2	121		
	424	8.95	44 (tiles only)
Roof of plain concrete tiles			
Roof timber and construction	303		
Tiles, felt and battens, fitted 48 m^2 at £4.21/m^2	202		
	505	10.50	68 (tiles only)

Table 3 shows that except for the roof and first floor, partitions are the only other single item in a house that account for a substantial quantity of timber. Although a grg school partition system that satisfied all the requirments of the DES performance specification was developed by BRS[4], it seems unlikely that a grg or grc house partition that would compete in price with plasterboard stud partition will be developed. In any case, there are already alternative partitions that use no timber.

Whilst other timber components in houses utilise relatively little timber, grc still has potential as a substitute material and a prototype grc window-frame has been made by BRS and further developed by one of Pilkington's licencees. Its cost lies about half-way between that of timber and aluminium windows, and it is attractive for use in high-rise buildings where its freedom from maintenance requirements is an asset.

One area where fibre reinforced composites are unable to compete with timber, despite its rising cost, is for wooden doors. These are still remarkably cheap and alternative materials are unlikely to displace them. For fire-resistant doors however, grg seems to be an ideal material, and a low density form of it has been used as the core of a 43 mm thick door that satisfied the requirements for a one-hour fire-check door, when tested in accordance with BS 476:Pt 8. The only timber used for this door was for a decorative veneer and lipping.

This work is part of a continuing programme of research and development at BRE on composite materials and components. Whilst it is not intended to convey the impression that all the components described are commercially available, it is worth noting that they are rather more than a gleam in the designer's eye as is borne out by the activities of Pilkington Brothers Ltd and their 100 or so licensees in the UK and overseas in developing grc components in building, including its use as a replacement for timber pallets, window frames and formwork. The involvement of this large number of commercial firms is probably an adequate commentary on the economic viability of fibre reinforced inorganic composites.

REFERENCES

1   British Patents No 1200732 1970
                        1243972 1971
                        1243973 1971

2   **Majumdar, A J** and **Ryder, J F.** Glass Technology, Vol 9, No 3, 1968, pp 78-84

3   British Patent (Provisional) No. 1573/74.

4   **Ryder, J F.** Proceedings of International Building Exhibition Concerence, pp 69-89, HMSO, 1972.

   Other reading:

   Steele, B R. Proceedings of International Building Exhibition Conference, p 9, HMSO, 1972.

   Grimer, F J and **Ali, M A.** Concrete Research, Vol 21, May 1969, p 23.

   Majumdar, A J and **Nurse, R W.** Materials Science and Engineering, Vol 15, Nos 2-3, pp 107-127.

   Gutt, W. 6th CIB Congress. 1974.

APPENDIX - Transcript of Discussion on Paper

Question

There are just two points. First of all, I wonder if any attempts have been made to assess the total energy input required to make the various new fibre composite materials. I include of course the mining energy, for as in the case of forestry, one must include the energy required to do the forestry and harvesting procedures. Secondly, I wonder whether the long term resistance to continual stress of these materials is thoroughly well assessed. The recent collapses of school roofs, caused I believe by the failure of high alumina-cement concrete under continuous loading, does make one wonder whether the long term resistance of materials such as gypsum or even glass to continual fairly high level stressing has been examined.

Answer

In reply to the first part of the question, this type of assessment is being carried out at PRL for building materials in general. As has been said, even for highly energy intensive materials such as cement the cost of the energy is still only about 20 per cent of the material cost. However, this energy has to be paid for one way or another, and this is reflected in the price of the material. If the energy content of a building material is high, and the price of energy is high then that material will become uneconomical and will not be used to anything like the same extent that it would have been otherwise.

In answer to the second point, whenever any new material or product is developed, it obviously has to go through a very thorough and searching examination into its durability and its long term performance and the materials which I have been describing are no exception in this respect. We have specimens and components of grc exposed to natural weathering on sites in this country and, in collaboration with Pilkington Brothers, throughout the world. We also have some specimens weathering under stress and these tests are supplemented by laboratory creep and fatigue tests under various environmental conditions. At the present time we do not recommend grc for fully structural applications as we have not enough evidence, or at least we have not enough long term experience to define the safety limits of its use. These materials have been under intensive investigation for only about five years so they cannot be yet considered for fully structural applications where one is looking for a life of 20, 30, 40, 50 years. But there are many other non-structural applications where they can replace timber, such as window frames, doors, pallets and so on where their potential as replacements for timber can be fully exploited.

Question

This is not a point I make on behalf of my Department at all, it is just a personal one which I do not think any of the previous speakers have brought out. That is the cost of the components and of building represented by the cost of labour associated with operations in timber; for instance the wages of carpenters are rising rapidly. I wonder whether this might not be a factor in favouring the development and use of the kind of fibrous composite materials described to us.

Answer

We have not looked into this in great detail yet, but I think the indications are that these new components may well have a comparatively small site labour content - certainly the complete purlin roof can be very quickly erected. The questioner has brought out a valuable point, but the labour required to manufacture such components will obviously depend on the extent to which the process can be mechanised.

Glass fibre reinforced autoclaved calcium silicate insulation material (CP 62/74)

J.M. West, K. Speakman and A.J. Majumdar

INTRODUCTION

Autoclaved calcium silicate materials are used in the construction industry as sand lime bricks and lightweight insulation materials. In the latter use if strengthening of the product is required, this is commonly achieved by reinforcement with asbestos fibres. Asbestos reinforced insulation board is extensively used as a partition material on ships where its lightness and fire resisting properties are particularly beneficial. In this application, the autoclaved calcium silicate material reinforced with asbestos is faced on both sides by laminates of plastics. The passenger cabins in ships are fitted out with such a material. The finished laminates must possess adequate screw holding capacity so that fixings such as wash basins can be conveniently attached to them.

Over the years a great deal of concern has been expressed about the use of asbestos fibres in their various applications. Gilson[1] has recently reviewed the position. It is believed that all types of commercially used asbestos can cause asbestosis and bronchial cancer provided they are inhaled in sufficient quantities and that fibres 5-100 mm in length with diameters less than about 2μm present the greatest danger. The use of asbestos in the partitions of ships' cabins has the additional hazard that such partitions are worked on (sawn, drilled etc) by operatives in the confined space of the cabins and the asbestos 'dust' which these operations are likely to produce may easily be inhaled in quantities exceeding the safe limits.

An attempt has been made to explore the potentialities of alkali-resistant Cem-FIL glass fibres in replacing asbestos reinforcements in autoclaved calcium silicate materials. In the first instance effort was concentrated on developing a material with properties similar to those of the asbestos board but in which the asbestos fibres are completely replaced by alkali-resistant glass fibres. Such material has now been produced and the results of a selection from the various experiments carried out in connection with this development are described in this report.

MATERIALS

Silica and hydrated lime formed the main constituents of the matrix. In some boards a small quantity (5-20 per cent by weight) of ordinary Portland Cement (OPC) was also added. The reinforcing glass fibre was supplied as roving consisting of 29 strands each having 204 filaments of 13μm diameter.

Silica was introduced either as ground sand or as kieselguhr or as a mixture of the two in equal molar proportions. The ground sand had a specific surface area of 262 m^2/kg and gave α-quartz as the only crystalline phase upon X-ray examination. In the hydrated lime, $Ca(OH)_2$ was the only crystalline phase detected by X-rays, apart from a trace of calcite.

While comparing the properties of glass fibre reinforced calcium silicate (grcs) with those of asbestos board it became quite clear that the screw-holding capacity of the former was insufficient. Attempts were then made to overcome this deficiency by various means. Wood pulp (25 per cent long fibre coniferous, 40 per cent short fibre deciduous, 35 per cent mill broke), vermiculite packing material (passing 1/8 in. sieve) and polypropylene fibres were used in these experiments. The polymer fibre was 152 μm (0.006 in.) in diameter.

Tables 1-4 include details of the compositions of the boards produced. The CaO/SiO_2 molar ratios of these boards ranged from 0.8-1.2 although most of the boards produced contained CaO and SiO_2 in the nominal ratio of 1.0.

FABRICATION

The spray suction technique developed at BRE and described elsewhere[2] was used to make boards which were mostly about 8 mm thick. When kieselguhr was used the mixture was prepared the day before and stood overnight. When small quantities of OPC had to be added, they were mixed in immediately before spraying. The glass roving was chopped continuously to produce 34 mm long strands and these were sprayed simultaneously with the pumped slurry of lime and silica onto the suction bed. The spraying and chopping apparatus traverses automatically across the suction bed, covering an adjacent strip during each pass. The fibres lie approximately parallel to the plane of the mould, but are otherwise randomly orientated. For the production of very thick boards (for example 20 mm thick) the suction mould was built up at the edges and two complete layers of slurry and glass were sprayed onto it. The boards were either 4 m or 1.5 m long and approximately 1 m wide.

AUTOCLAVING

Initial tests were made using a Farnell autoclave (designated 'F' in the tables) with an internal diameter of 193 mm. Approximately two litres of water inside the vessel were used to distribute the heat from the external electric elements. The sheet to be autoclaved was cut into 130 x 155 mm rectangles with the corners trimmed off sufficiently to allow the remainder to fit the vessel. The samples were placed horizontally on copper sheets which were supported one above the other with small gaps in between. Although some specimens were successfully cured in this way, many specimens expanded and lost all cohesiveness, probably as a result of too much heat reaching them directly through the cylinder walls, rather than via the heated steam. The small capacity of the vessel, and the lack of a pressure switch to control the curing conditions were other disadvantages with the autoclave.

A larger autoclave (designated 'IM' in the tables), which had an internal diameter of 590 mm was also used in the programme. Heat was distributed by water, heated by immersed electric elements sealed inside the vessel, and controlled by an adjustable pressure switch. This proved to be a much more satisfactory system for curing the material. The sheet to be autoclaved was cut into 330 x 460 mm rectangles and supported on a brass sheet. It was found to be convenient and satisfactory to stack several sheets horizontally on top of each other for curing. The filter paper which remained attached to the demoulded sheet prevented adjacent sheets cementing together.

For experiments requiring larger areas of sheeting, an autoclave having internal dimensions of 2.5 x 1.2 m was used (designated 'ST' in the tables). This was heated by steam, piped from a boiler with an adjustable pressure control. The grcs sheets were supported on steel sheets or asbestos board. Handling was very difficult with sheets this size, as it was hard to avoid disrupting the matrix prior to curing. Invisible handling damage may have contributed to some unexpectedly low strength values for sheeting cured in this autoclave.

It was found, using all these autoclaves, that the freshly made sheet was difficult to handle, and tended to expand and develop little strength during autoclaving. Sheet up to 400 mm long which had been allowed to dry until it reduced in weight by about 15 per cent, was easy to handle, was dimensionally stable during autoclaving, and usually developed good strength. Before autoclaving most 'green' boards were dried at room temperature for two days, normally losing about 15 per cent of their weight, though sometimes much more. Except for some earlier mixes sheets which could not be autoclaved immediately were covered up with polythene sheet or sealed in polythene bags to exclude carbon dioxide. To investigate the effect of storage prior to autoclaving, a comparative test was made (batch 2, Table 1) in which four sheets were first stored for two days in the laboratory atmosphere during which time they lost about 15 per cent of their weight. Two of these sheets (2d) were subsequently stored in a polythene bag, stopping further water loss. The other two sheets (2c) were allowed to dry further for seven days after which they had lost 57 per cent of their initial weight. The four sheets were autoclaved together and the physical properties measured later showed no significant differences between specimens given the two treatments. A similar test on another board revealed a slight drop in the ultimate strength obtained after boards had been allowed to lose 56 per cent of their initial weight before curing. Storing for long periods under conditions where exposure to CO_2 took place caused much carbonation of the lime and a large reduction in the strength achieved after autoclaving. For most of the data given differences in storage before curing are unlikely to have been important in determining the ultimate strengths obtained.

In the tables of results the autoclave regime is only described in terms of the peak operating temperature and the lengths of time over which this temperature was maintained. Heating up of the two smaller autoclaves, 'F' and 'IM', from $100^{o}C$ to the peak operating temperature, and cooling subsequently to $100^{o}C$ generally took 1-2 hours for each operation. The largest autoclave, 'ST', generally took 2-3 hours to heat up and 5-6 hours to cool. In a few cases specimens were autoclaved for a second time, indicated by two entries for autoclaving time.

Table 1 The composition, treatment and physical properties of grcs boards

Ref No	Raw materials in addition to hydrated lime	CaO/SiO$_2$ molar ratio	Glass fibre content 34 mm (kg/m^3)	Glass fibre (vol%)	Precuring: Storage time (days)	Precuring: Drying loss (% weight)	Autoclave: Temperature (°C)	Autoclave: Time (h)	Autoclave: Vessel	Density (kg/m^3)	Modulus of rupture Dry (MN/m^2)	Modulus of rupture Wet (MN/m^2)	Impact strength Dry (kJ/m^2)	Impact strength Wet (kJ/m^2)	Screw pulling resistance Dry (MN/m^2)	Screw pulling resistance Wet (MN/m^2)	Phases identified in the autoclaved products
1a	Quartz	1.0	74	2.9	7	~15	150	6	F	~950	8.3	7.1	6.6	8.0	–	–	Q CH C (tr)
b	"	"	"	"	9	~15	170–180	16	F	–	5.6	5.3	1.5	1.5	–	–	Tob Q C (tr)
2a	Kieselguhr	0.8	71	2.8	2	16	180	10	IM	550	7.3	6.4	9.0	10.3	1.4	1.3	Tob CSH C Q (tr)
b	"	"	"	"	2	15	"	10+10	"	540	7.8	7.0	8.7	9.2	1.6	1.4	Tob C Q (tr)
c	"	"	"	"	9	57	"	20	"	570	7.1	5.9	8.9	9.1	1.6	1.2	" " (1)
d	"	"	"	"	9	15	"		"	540	7.1	6.0	7.8	8.7	1.5	1.3	" " (1)
3a	"	1.0	78	3.0	2	17	"	10	"	590	7.9	6.9	6.9	8.4	1.7	1.4	" " –
b	"	"	"	"	2	17	"	10+10	"	560	8.2	7.2	7.9	7.7	1.7	1.5	" " Q (tr)
c	"	"	"	"	9	56	"	20	"	590	6.9	6.1	7.5	7.8	1.6	1.2	" " –
d	"	"	"	"	9	16	"	"	"	570	8.0	6.4	5.9	4.9	1.7	1.4	" " –
4	" + 5% OPC	"	72	2.8	2	15	"	10	"	630	6.6	5.9	6.0	5.5	1.6	1.6	CSH CH C V Q (tr)
5	" + 20% OPC	"	69	2.7	2	14	"	"	"	740	6.2	6.2	4.7	3.7	1.7	1.7	CH CSH C V Q (tr)
6a	" + 10% OPC	"	104	4.0	4	~5	150	4.3	"	660	6.6	7.3	7.0	9.2	1.4	–	CSH C V Q (tr)
b	"	"	"	"	5	~10	180	3	ST	650	7.1	7.2	5.7	6.6	1.5	–	
7	"	"	88	3.4	1	~2	170	3	"	620	5.0	3.7	5.2	5.6	–	–	
8	"	"	88	3.4	5	~10	160	2	IM	610	6.1	5.4	7.5	9.7	1.4	–	
9	"	"	30	1.2	7	52	180	10	"	590	2.2	1.7	3.5	3.3	0.9	–	
10	"	"	63	2.5	6	40	"	"	"	590	4.9	3.9	6.0	5.9	0.9	–	
11	"	"	168	6.5	15	54	"	"	"	650	10.5	8.8	16.1	15.4	1.8	–	Tob C Q
12a	Qu + Kies	0.8	83	3.3	1	6	"	"	"	720	7.8	6.8	8.3	9.0	1.7	–	
b	"	"	"	"	16	45	"	8	ST	730	8.4	7.9	6.6	7.2	2.1	–	
13	"	1.2	84	3.3	6	34	"	"	"	800	5.2	5.8	2.6	3.8	1.7	–	C Q V
14a	" + 10% OPC	0.8	77	3.0	8	37	"	10	IM	750	8.6	7.3	6.0	6.5	2.3	–	Tob Q C V (tr)
b	"	"	"	"	8	35	"	8	ST	760	5.8	5.5	4.2	5.3	1.6	–	C V Q Tob (tr)
15	"	1.2	80	3.1	6	38	150	4.7	IM	800	7.1	5.5	6.2	6.1	1.2	–	Q C V A CH
16a	"	1.0	83	3.2	1	9	"	4.7+15	"	–	–	8.0	–	8.8	–	1.4	CH Q CSH C (2) (3)
b	"	"	"	"	1	9	160	4.5	"	840	–	7.2	–	3.8	–	1.9	Q CSH CH C (2)
c	"	"	"	"	9	17	"		"	–	–	7.6	–	8.3	–	–	CH Q CSH V C (2)

The material was 7–9.5 mm thick except for batch 8 which was 15 mm thick. (1) A weak line was detected at 15Å which could possibly indicate the presence of Z-phase[10,11]. (2) Unidentified weak lines were found at 9.75 Å (CSH II?) and 2.09Å. (3) Unidentified weak lines were found at 5.61 and 3.29Å.

EVALUATION OF PROPERTIES

A Physical and mechanical properties

(a) Density

Weights and volumes of specimens were determined experimentally and densities were calculated using at least two specimens per batch. Before testing, half of the specimens were usually dried out to their approximate equilibrium weight in a 40°C oven provided with a circulating fan. A period of two days was the normal time allowed, though specimens rarely lost significant weight after one day. The test specimens usually had square edges, allowing a reasonable assessment of volume to be made from their dimensions. Several measurements were taken on each specimen. The range of dimensions on each specimen usually varied by $\leq \pm 5$ per cent of the mean for thickness and $\leq \pm 1$ per cent of the mean for width.

(b) Modulus of rupture

For thinner sheets (Tables 1-3) the modulus of rupture (MOR) was calculated from values of maximum loads determined on 50 x 150 mm specimens tested under four-point loading on a span of 135 mm using an Instron testing machine. A constant cross-head speed of 2 mm per minute was used for all bending tests. Specimens were mostly tested in batches of six and they were chosen from evenly distributed areas of the autoclaved sheets. The sheets were cut up while they were still wet using a masonry saw and dried in a 40°C oven before testing. Some specimens were also tested wet.

For specimens where the thickness exceeded 1/12 of the span of 135 mm, a new test rig was designed. In the new rig there are two available spans, either 362 mm or 230 mm. The rollers are 40 mm in diameter and can be arranged in either a three-point or a four-point loading configuration. The 230 mm span and 40 mm roller diameter were adopted in order for them to be approximately similar to those of the MOR rigs recommended by the British Standards Institution[3]. The main difference between the rigs is that the new BRS device can only take specimens up to about 70 mm wide, whereas the British Standards rig referred to is designed to take specimens 254 mm (10 in.) square. A few tests were made on 10 in. square specimens using such a rig, which was loaded by a lever arm mechanism.

(c) Impact strength

The ends from four specimens from each batch of six tested on the Instron for their bending strength were impact tested on an Izod swinging-pendulum type machine. Impact strength (IS) values were calculated from the breadth, depth and impact reading. The specimens were clamped in such a way that approximately 40 mm of the specimen projected above the jaws of the retaining clamp and was in the path of the pendulum. The top faces of both ends of two of the specimens were struck by the pendulum, whereas in the case of the other two specimens the bottom faces of both ends were struck.

Striking the top of one end of a specimen and the bottom of the other end was avoided because it usually led to either two high or two low IS values being obtained, depending on which way the fibres are angled with respect to the plane of the board. In addition, there was sometimes a top and bottom effect caused by a greater concentration of either fibres or slurry near one face of the specimens. Standard deviations can be calculated from the eight results, but it is felt that the values might be misleading since usually four results were high and four were low, reflecting the variations caused by the method of fabrication.

(d) Screw pulling resistance

The thickness of most boards used for the determination of screw pulling resistance (SPR) was about 8 mm. With these thin boards a hole was drilled completely through the test specimen using a 1/8 in. diameter drill, then a No 8 gauge $1\frac{1}{2}$ in. self-tapping screw was screwed through the hole until four threads were exposed on the far side. The specimen was restrained by a short section of pvc pipe of external diameter 50 mm and internal diameter 40 mm. A steadily increasing axial load was applied to the underside of the screw head by means of a stirrup.

The apparatus used to apply the load was a modified lever arm tensile testing machine with a nominal loading rate of 1 kg/second up to 120 kg.

For some of the specimens from thicker boards the test method recommended by BSRA* was adopted. This method employed a similar self-tapping screw which was screwed into the specimen to within 1/8 in. of the reverse side of the material. Data obtained by this method can be found in

---

* British Ship Research Association.

Table 2   The effect of additives upon screw pulling resistance in grcs boards

Ref No	Raw materials in addition to hydrated lime	Glass fibre content 34 mm (kg/m³)	(vol%)	Special additives	Drying loss before curing (% weight)	Autoclave regime Temp (°C)	Time (h)	Density (kg/m³)	MOR Dry (MN/m²)	IS Dry (kJ/m²)	Mean SPR (kN)	Number of tests	Dry Thickness (mm)	Dry Mean SPR (MN/m²)	Wet Mean SPR (MN/m²)	Phases identified in the autoclaved products
1	Quartz + Kies + 10%OPC	78	3.0	-	34	180	10	740	6.3 (1)	-	0.93	2	19.5	1.9	-	Tob CSH C Q (2)
2	"	82	3.2	36kg/m³ 6mm gf (1.4vol%)	39	"	"	820	8.9	5.2	0.29	4	7.6	2.8	-	
3a	Kies + 10% OPC	78	3.0	5% dry weight vermiculite	~25	150	10	600	5.9	4.4	0.15	4	8.7	1.1	0.9	
b	"	"	"	"	~25	180	20	570	6.6	3.4	0.16	4	8.6	1.3	0.9	
4a	"	79	3.1	7kg/m³ 6mm ppf (0.8vol%)	15	150	10	620	6.4	4.7	0.16	6	8.2	1.3	0.9	CSH C V(tr) CH(tr) Q(tr)
b	"	"	"	"	15	160	"	620	6.6	4.3	0.15	6	8.0	1.3	0.9	"
c	"	"	"	"	14	180	20	590	5.9	3.7	0.18	4	8.3	1.6	1.2	Tob CSH C Q(tr)
5	"	88	3.4	5% dry weight wood pulp	37	"	"	570	7.7	5.9	0.18	4	7.5	1.7	1.3	"
6a	Kieselguhr only	72	2.8	15kg/m³ 51mm ppf (1.7vol%)	11	160	21	550	5.1	7.9	0.21	6	10.1	1.3	0.9	CSH C
b	"	"	"	"	14	170	20	550	5.8	8.8	0.25	6	10.1	1.6	1.0	Tob C Q(tr) V(tr)

All mixes had a CaO/SiO$_2$ molar ratio of 1.0. All the boards were cured in autoclave 'TM' 3–11 days after they were sprayed (gf = glass fibre and ppf = polypropylene fibre).
(1) The MOR test was made using a span of 135 mm. (2) A very weak line was present at 9.7 Å.

145

Table 3 The durability of grcs boards

Ref No	Raw materials in addition to hydrated lime	Glass fibre content 34 mm (kg/m³)	34 mm (Vol %)	6 mm (kg/m³)	6 mm (Vol %)	Precuring Storage time (days)	Drying loss (% weight)	Autoclave Temperature (°C)	Time (hr)	Vessel	Storage Time (days)	Conditions (at 20°C)	Density (kg/m³)	MOR (MN/m²)	IS (kJ/m²)	SPR (MN/m²)	Phases identified in the autoclave products
1a	Quartz only	74	2.9			37	~20	150	10.5	F	1	Wet	950	6.0	3.5	–	Q C A (tr) CH (tr)
b	"	74	2.9			37	~20	150	10.5	F	795	Dry	950	5.6	3.2	2.3	
c	"	74	2.9			37	~20	150	10.5	F	795	Wet	950	6.7	–	2.2	Q CH C
d	"	74	2.9			14	~15	150–180	4	F	3	Dry	950	7.1	4.6	2.7	
e	"	74	2.9			7	~20	150	6	F	13	Dry	950	8.3	6.6	–	
f	"	74	2.9			9	~5	170–180	16	F	5	Dry	950	5.5	1.5	–	Tob Q C (tr)
2a	Quartz + Kies + 10% OPC	83	3.2			16	15	160	4.5	IM	12	Dry	840	8.4	7.9	–	
b	"	83	3.2			16	15	160	4.5	IM	5	Wet	840	7.8	7.7	–	Q CH CSH C (tr)
c	"	83	3.2			16	15	160	4.5	IM	265	Wet	840	8.3	7.2	2.2	
d	"	83	3.2			21	17	150	4.7	IM	7	Wet	840	7.4	9.0	–	Q CH CSH (tr)
e	"	83	3.2			21	17	150	4.7	IM	260	Wet	840	8.0	13.6	1.7	
3a	"	82	3.2	36	1.4	7	37	180	8	ST	Storage sequence (days): 20 Dry 40°C / 2 Dry 40°C / 5 Dry 40°C		820	8.3	4.3	2.1	
b	"	82	3.2	36	1.4	7	37	180	8	ST	20 " / 2 Tap water / 5 "		820	9.2	4.6	2.2	
c	"	82	3.2	36	1.4	7	37	180	8	ST	20 " / 2 Sea water / 5 "		820	9.1	4.3	2.5	
d	"	82	3.2	36	1.4	7	37	180	8	ST	20 " / 2 Tap water / 5 Tap water		820	8.3	5.4	1.3	

All mixes had a CaO/SiO$_2$ molar ratio of 1.0 and all boards were 7 – 10 mm thick.

Table 4 under 'partial penetration'. To compare the results obtained with specimens of different thickness, it was assumed that a simple relationship $S \propto \frac{w}{d^2}$ (where S is the SPR, w the load at failure and d the depth of penetration of the screw) is applicable. This assumption is based on the observation that at failure an approximately cone-shaped piece of material usually comes away with the screw. If the solid angle subtended by the cone is taken to be constant for a given type of specimen, the area of the fractured surface produced by the cone is proportional to the square of the height of the cone (or the depth of screw penetration).

For the thinner specimens where the screw passed completely through the sheet, the formula was modified, to allow for the imaginary portion of the cone beyond the back surface of the specimen, to

$$S = \frac{w}{(d + x)^2 - x^2}$$

(where x is the apparent distance beyond the back surface of the specimen to which the cone extends). In most cases x was estimated to be about 3 mm and this figure was used when calculating SPR. All the results given in the tables were calculated using this latter formula unless otherwise specified.

In this exercise on the determination of SPR in grcs boards, six samples were commonly used in each experiment. Of these, four were the broken ends of specimens from the MOR test, the other two not having undergone any form of testing previously. For three of the tests, screws were introduced into the material from the 'top' face, and the remaining three from the 'bottom' face. In any one piece of material one test was from the 'top' and one from the 'bottom'.

B Thermal and fire properties

(a) Thermal conductivity

Ten specimens 304.8 mm square and 8 mm thick (6a, Table 1) were prepared and were tested according to the procedure detailed in BS874, section 10a. Each test specimen consisted of a pile of five boards.

(b) Fire resistance

Two 914.4 mm square panels (7 and 8, Table 1) were tested in a small furnace at the Fire Research Station, Borehamwood, Herts, according to the procedures of BS476. The thicker board (8) had been allowed to dry in the laboratory for ten days after autoclaving before the fire test.

C Durability

(a) Retention of strength of grcs boards with time

Almost half of the specimens prepared for testing were distributed between a 40 per cent humidity room on ventilated shelving, and a 90 per cent humidity room in tanks of water (20°C). Very few of these specimens have been tested yet but they are available for studying long term durability. One batch of specimens was subjected to short term wetting and drying to determine the effect of this treatment on strength (3, Table 3).

(b) Retention of fibre strength after autoclaving

When the first board was made, tests were carried out to determine the residual strength of fibres removed from the board after autoclaving. These were compared with fibres from strands exposed only to the steam in the autoclave, and with unheated fibres. The autoclaved specimens were split as nearly as possible along the centre of the plane of the board, using a hardened steel wedge. Individual fibres were removed for testing, taking care that the central zones to be stressed were not touched during manipulation. The fibres were tested on a modified laboratory balance[4]. The load at failure was recorded for each fibre, and the diameter measured (using a Watson Image Splitting Eyepiece). The tensile strength at failure of each fibre was calculated.

D Other properties

Two grcs sheets approximately 1.5 x 1 m x 20 mm in size and having densities of 600 and 800 kg/m³ were taken to a British shipyard to be planed and bonded with a suitable plastic laminate. Flexural and screwholding tests were applied to these sheets. Because of their considerable thickness the larger MOR test rig was used at a span of 230 mm.

Samples of thick laminated and unlaminated material were worked in the shipyard using four common joinery machines. Samples of dust were taken while machining both grcs and commercially available asbestos boards using a personal air sampler, a cascade impactor and a cascade centripeter and were examined by the Medical and Health Physics Division of the UK Atomic Energy Research Establishment, Harwell. A summary of this report has been given elsewhere[5].

Table 4 The effect of lamination on fibre reinforced calcium silicate boards

Ref No	Raw materials in addition to hydrated lime and 10% OPC	Glass fibre content 34 mm (kg/m³)	(vol%)	Curing time (hrs)	Condition when tested	Finish	Net dry density (kg/m³)	Modulus of rupture test Span (mm)	Width (mm)	Depth (mm)	MOR (MN/m²)	Impact strength (kJ/m²)	Screw pulling resistance through penetration (thickness) (mm)	Mean SPR (MN/m²)	partial penetration (mm)	Mean SPR (MN/m²)
1a	Quartz + Kies	78	3.0	21	dry	Plain	740	135	51	19.5	5.4	–	19.5	1.7	17.6	2.1
b	"	"	"	"	"	Laminated	940	"	"	18.7	11.3	–	18.7	2.8	16.3	2.3
c	"	"	"	"	"	Plain	–	230	254	16.0	5.9	–	–	–	–	–
d	"	"	"	"	"	Laminated	–	"	"	18.7	18.0	–	–	–	–	–
2a	Kieselguhr only	74	2.9	8	"	Laminated	780	"	"	19.9	10.6	–	–	–	–	–
b	"	"	"	"	"	Plain	580	135	"	19.1	4.6	–	19.1	1.0	16.5	1.5
c	"	"	"	"	"	Laminated	780	"	"	19.9	9.5	–	19.9	3.1	17.0	1.8
3a	(Asbestos board)	–	–	–	"	Plain	690	230	"	9.1	6.9	2.6	9.1	3.6	–	–
b	"	–	–	–	"	Laminated	900	"	"	12.4	53.1	8.9	12.5	6.7	–	–
c	"	–	–	–	wet	Plain	690	"	"	9.1	6.6	–	–	–	–	–
d	"	–	–	–	"	Laminated	900	"	"	12.4	43.3	–	–	–	–	–

All grcs boards had a CaO/SiO$_2$ mix of molar ratio 1.0 including 10% by weight of OPC. They were all autoclaved for 6–8 days after spraying and had lost about 30% of their initial weight by drying. They were all cured at 180°C in the largest autoclave (ST).

E Phase characterisation

Materials from several batches of autoclaved grcs were ground to pass a BS 100 mesh sieve and subjected to both X-ray powder analysis and differential thermal analysis (DTA). A Guinier focusing camera was used to record the X-ray diffraction patterns produced. DTAs were carried out on samples of about 0.2 g in open ceramic vessels using quartz as a reference with a heating rate of about 10°C/minute.

RESULTS AND DISCUSSION

A Physical and mechanical properties

The results of the present study are summarised in Tables 1-4. Unmodified grcs boards were produced with a density range of 420 to 900 kg/m^3 (26 to 56 lb/ft^2). The lowest density obtained with a reasonable strength was 540 kg/m^3 in a board consisting only of hydrated lime, kieselguhr and glass fibre (2.8 per cent by volume). Compared with other grcs boards, this was exceptionally strong for such a low density, for example one batch (2b, Table 1) gave an MOR value of 7.8 MN/m^2 and an SPR value of 1.6 MN/m^2.

Strength values have been obtained ranging between 1.16 and 10.45 MN/m^2 for MOR, 1.48 and 16.10 kJ/m^2 for IS, and 0.31 and 2.83 MN/m^2 for SPR. These values can generally be seen to vary as a function of density, fibre content, curing conditions and composition. The coefficient of variation of most results fell between 10 and 20 per cent of the mean for MOR and 5 and 15 per cent for SPR.

The great majority of MOR values of specimens with a glass content of 2.7 - 3.1 per cent by volume, fell between 5 and 9 MN/m^2. Generally batches with lower densities and those cured at lower temperatures for short periods of time fell at the lower end of this range (eg 3a, Table 2) while those having higher density and receiving longer curing times at higher temperatures fell towards the top of the range (eg 14a, Table 1). The properties of one board can be used to illustrate the effect of different curing conditions. Part of one board, (3, Table 2) sections of which were cured at two different temperatures, was stronger (except for IS) when heated at a higher temperature for a longer time. Comparisons of curing conditions between autoclaves are not straightforward. The previous example (14a, Table 1) contrasts in strength with part of the same board cured for a similar time period and at the same temperature in a different autoclave (ST) where the strength values are low (14b, Table 1). Material cured in the larger autoclave (ST) did not always give poorer results (see 12, Table 1).

Some of the boards, particularly those containing quartz rather than kieselguhr (eg 1b, Table 1) lost strength when autoclaved at temperatures exceeding about 170°C for an extended period of time. The IS was much lower than that obtained for comparable specimens which had a shorter curing at lower temperatures (eg 1a, Table 1) and the MOR slightly lower, whereas the SPR may well have been improved. The effect of longer curing at higher temperatures on IS and SPR are likely to be the result of increased bonding between the fibres and the matrix, the quartz-containing boards giving a good bond more readily than those containing only kieselguhr. These effects can also be seen in a mixed quartz-kieselguhr board (eg 16a and b, Table 1).

Present results indicate that the MOR and IS of grcs boards varied directly with the glass fibre content in the range 1.2 to 6.5 per cent by volume as illustrated in Figures 1 and 2. The SPR on

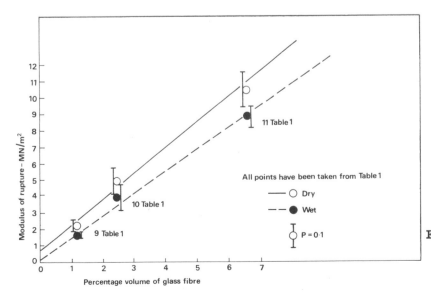

Figure 1 The variation of MOR with glass fibre content

149

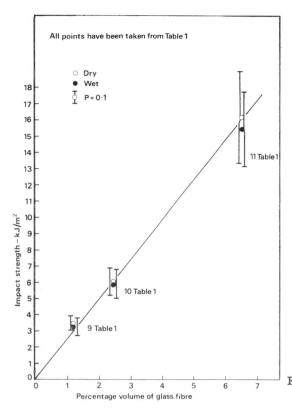

Figure 2 The variation of impact strength with glass fibre content

the other hand was not improved in a similar way with increase in glass content (see Figure 3 points from Table 1).

Since the grcs boards having different CaO/SiO$_2$ molar ratios (C/S) could not be prepared with the same nominal glass content, it is strictly not possible to comment on the effect of mix composition on the properties of the grcs material. However, if it is assumed that the strength of grcs is proportional to the glass content, the properties of two batches which were cured together in autoclave IM can be compared, that is to say, batch 2, Table 1 and batch 3, Table 1 (C/S of 0.8 and 1.0 respectively). The former (C/S 0.8) gave better results on this basis, especially for IS. For boards cured in the largest autoclave (ST) it also appeared that a C/S of 0.8 was superior to one of 1.2 (compare 12b with 13, Table 1) except when they contained OPC (compare 14b and 15).

Results for boards produced in autoclave IM indicated that the presence of OPC in the matrix generally produced a slight increase in SPR and a large decrease in IS while having little effect on MOR (compare 3a with 4 and with 5, and compare 12a with 14a in Table 1). This suggests that OPC had increased the bond between the matrix and the fibre. It also increased the density. The presence of OPC in boards cured in the autoclave which had a longer warming up period (ST)

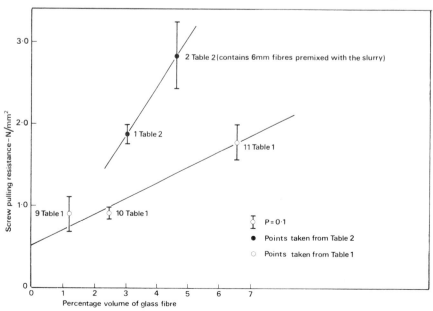

Figure 3 The variation of screw pulling resistance with glass fibre content

led to a worsening of all strength properties when the C/S was 0.8 (compare 12b with 14b) but not when the C/S was 1.2 (compare 13 with 15).

In order to improve the SPR of grcs boards it was thought worthwhile to pre-mix a certain proportion of the glass fibre with the matrix and incorporate the remainder by spraying in the usual way. Only short fibres can be pre-mixed easily and the result obtained with 6 mm fibres is seen in Figure 3. The board designated as 1, Table 2, contained 3.0 vol per cent of fibre which was introduced by spraying only. The board 2 of Table 2 was prepared in a similar way but an additional 1.4 vol per cent glass was incorporated in this board by pre-mixing. From the slopes of the two lines in Figure 3 it appears that pre-mixing might have had the desired effect as far as improving the screw pulling resistance is concerned.

Other attempts to improve the screw pulling strength were not very successful. Pre-mixed vermiculite (5 per cent dry weight; 3, Table 2) or pre-mixed polypropylene fibre (6 mm long; 4, Table 2) did not improve the SPR of the board. Polypropylene degrades at $180^{o}C$ and therefore could not have contributed to SPR after autoclaving at the temperature (4c, Table 2). Samples containing wood pulp (5 per cent dry weight; 5, Table 2) showed some improvement when dry but this was lost in wet storage. The incorporation of long (51 mm) polypropylene fibres in grcs (6, Table 2) by spraying was also not helpful in this respect, although polypropylene fibres taken from boards autoclaved at $170^{o}C$ were still strong.

B Thermal and fire properties

The thermal conductivity was found to be 0.100 $W/m^{o}C$ (0.69 Btu. in./$ft^{2}h^{o}F$). This is well within the limit of 0.144 $W/m^{o}C$ required by the British Standards for insulating board[3]. Some of the lower density boards produced (eg 2, Table 1) would have been even better insulators than this particular example whose density as tested was 657 kg/m^{3}.

The results of the fire test are summarised in Table 5. After 60 minutes there were no signs of cracking in either case, nor was there any flame penetration. The panels bowed slightly during the test and cracked to some extent on cooling, but they remained strong and did not disintegrate. The external face of the thicker board remained at a temperature of approximately $100^{o}C$ for 17 minutes, suggesting that a considerable amount of uncombined water was being vaporised from the board, though part of this would be interlayer water released from the calcium silicate hydrate matrix on the heated face of the board.

Steam was the only visible emission from the board during the test. Other studies, including differential thermal analysis, showed that the only other substance to be released when the material is heated is carbon dioxide at about $750^{o}C$, from the small amount of calcium carbonate present.

C Durability

The relevant results on the durability of grcs boards are given in Table 3. The first board made retained its strength well up to 2 years in dry or wet conditions (1b and c). The SPR cannot be compared because it was not originally determined. In these specimens it was still good. Other specimens (2c and e) were stored for $8\frac{1}{2}$ months in water and appeared to have retained their strength well, though there is again no comparison for SPR. Wet storage does not appear to have weakened them except perhaps for SPR which is generally poorer in any specimens tested wet.

Soaking in sea water or tap water followed by drying out again appear not to harm grcs (3b and c). They actually appear to have a higher MOR after this drying treatment. Specimens still wet when tested however had a slightly higher IS and a considerably lower SPR (3d) suggesting perhaps a weakened fibre matrix bond in the presence of water. A comparison of dry and wet strength data in Table 1 supports this conclusion though SPR has not been reduced so much by wet storage. The data in Table 1 additionally show a slight drop in MOR in most wet stored specimens.

Residual fibre strength is summarised in Table 6, contrasting strength values of fibres exposed to alkaline solutions in the boards, with strength values of 'steamed' and untreated fibres. In the specimens sampled (1, Table 3) the mean tensile strength of the fibres extracted from the boards was between 800-1200 MN/m^{2}, or a strength decrease from the untreated fibres of about 60-70 per cent.

The strength of these boards does not appear to be affected greatly by storage for two years, which suggests that the fibre strength changes little once autoclaving is complete. (In this case there was only a very small amount of free lime left after autoclaving.) Further strength tests at a later date on stored specimens would be necessary to confirm the good durability of the material, though there is no reason to suppose that grcs containing no free lime should not retain its strength almost indefinitely.

Table 5   Fire testing of glass reinforced calcium silicate board material

Two 3 ft x 3 ft panels were tested in a small furnace at the Fire Research Station, Borehamwood, Herts. To BS 476
Panel 1 6.5 – 7 mm thick (7 Table 1) $\Big\}$ same nominal composition
Panel 2 14.5 – 15 mm thick (8 Table 1)$\Big\}$

RESULTS

Time from start of test	Approximate mean temperatures °C					Temp limit after 15 min. Rule 50(2) merchant shipping rules	Mean temp after 15 min (32 min)	Approx time for the mean temp. to rise by 139°C
	5 min	10 min	30 min	(47 min)	60 min			
Hot face of board (furnace temp.) as BS curve	525	700	840		920	–	730°C	–
Panel 1 – external face	95	185	320		345	Average of 139°C above ambient temperature	278°C	–
Panel 2 – external face	45	90	102	(211)	230	Average of 139°C above ambient temperature	100°C (120°C)	36 (19) min

External temperatures given are the mean values recorded by three thermocouples distributed across the external face of the panels. The ambient temperature was approximately 25°C.

In panel 2 the temperature of the external face of the board remained at approximately 100°C for 17 minutes while uncombined water was vaporised from the board. Assuming the rise in temperature of the external face of the board has been delayed by about 17 minutes, then the values given in brackets are approximately those that would have been obtained when testing a board containing no uncombined water.

Table 6   Tensile strength of autoclaved and unautoclaved glass fibres used in grcs boards

Source or treatment	Regime		Fibre tensile strength		
	Temp °C	Time hrs	Mean MN/m^2	Standard Deviation	n
Autoclaved Board (1d Table 3)	150-180	4	850	212	10
Autoclaved Board (1e Table 3)	150	6	1219	149	15
Autoclaved Board (1f Table 3)	170-180	16	883	202	10
Strands exposed to steam	150-180	4	1823	264	5
	170-180	16	1929	901	5
Untreated strands	Room	–	2836	708	10

D Other properties

Since grcs is a new material a special adhesive had to be used for lamination. When the material was subsequently cut up in the shipyard, some debonding of the plastic sheeting occurred, from the face from which the cutter emerged. The effects of lamination on the MOR and SPR of the higher density boards can be seen by comparing the results given in Table 4 for the board alone (1a and c), and for the board laminated (1b and d). Similarly for the lower density board compare 2b with 2a and c. The effect of lamination on the MOR was to treble the strength, approximately, in the denser board and to double it in the less dense board. Failure during testing was by debonding of the plastic laminate. SPR was only slightly improved by lamination when tested according to BSRA methods.

Grcs machined well apart from the debonding of the laminate. Dust sampled was much the same as that from the asbestos board except that it lacked fibres of respirable size[5].

Lamination did not improve the properties of grcs as much as it does in the case of the denser asbestos board (compare 3a and c with 3b and d). The main reason for this appears to be the difficulty of bonding a surface layer to grcs. The spray suction process produces strengthening only in the plane of the board and therefore a tensile or shearing force at the surface acts chiefly on the weaker matrix. Adding some of the fibres as short lengths pre-mixed into the slurry would give an almost randomly orientated reinforcement with a much more intimate fibre/matrix interaction. This could improve surface bonding, as might a more deeply penetrating glue. Pre-mixed fibre boards were only made up in thin sheets not suitable for lamination, so there is no information on how effective this type of fabrication might be.

From the standpoint of health hazards grcs offers considerable advantages over the asbestos board, because although they both machine similarly, producing similar dust from the matrix, only the asbestos board releases the very harmful respirable fibres, and these in large quantities[5].

E   Phase characterisation

The results of the X-ray powder analysis are shown in Tables 1-3. The phases identified are placed in approximate order of abundance as indicated by the X-ray patterns obtained from the material. They are listed as Tob = 11.3 Å tobermorite, CSH = calcium silicate hydrate I and II, C = calcite, V = vaterite, A = aragonite, Q = quartz and CH = calcium hydroxide. When the X-ray patterns for a phase were very weak, this is indicated by the suffix (tr).

Specimens cured at 180°C mostly gave a sharp pattern for 11.3 Å tobermorite. (In commercially produced asbestos board tobermorite is also a principal constituent.) Those cured at 150°C did not give a line corresponding to 11.3 Å only a diffuse maxima at about 3.05 and 1.83 Å. The symbol CSH has been entered in the tables when these diffuse lines were present.

Autoclaved boards which contained ground sand in the intitial mix invariably retained enough unreacted quartz to give an X-ray pattern, but $Ca(OH)_2$ could not usually be detected in well autoclaved boards. $CaCO_3$ was always present due to CO_2 contamination, mostly as calcite, but sometimes as vaterite or aragonite.

The formation of xonotlite was expected[6], but its presence could not be established from X-ray powder lines, and studies using a scanning electron microscope showed little fibrous material of the type expected with xonotlite. Distinctive X-ray powder lines for scawtite, gyrolite, truscottite and dicalcium silicate alpha-hydrate were also absent.

All DTA curves gave a diffuse endothermic peak terminating at about 310°C and a sharp exotherm at about 840°C. The former is attributable to the loss of water from calcium silicate hydrates[7,8], and the latter to the formation of β wollastonite[8,9] from calcium silicate hydrates. In addition, the endotherm corresponding to the decarbonation of calcium carbonate was present. However in several cases two endothermic peaks appeared in this region at about 680°C and 770°C. Whether both of them were due to calcium carbonate in the sample having slightly different physical properties was not explored further.

REFERENCES

1 **Gilson, J C.** Health hazards of asbestos. Composites, Vol 3, 1972, p57.

2 British Patent Application No 4962/67: Gypsum Plaster Reinforced (1967).

3 **British Standards Institution**, BS3536:1962, Specification for Asbestos Insulating boards and Asbestos Wallboards.

4 **Gillet, R S** and **Majumdar, A J.** Apparatus for testing tensile strengths of corroded glass fibres. BRS Current Paper CP 26/68.

5 **Speakman, K** and **Majumdar, A J.** Health aspects of an asbestos board substitute. Paper presented at the Member firms' conference relating to accommodation bulkheads. British Ship Research Association, Wallsend Research Station, 12 June 1973.

6 **Midgley, H G** and **Chopra, S K.** Hydrothermal reactions between lime and aggregate fines. Magazine of Concrete Research, Vol 12, No 35, 1960, p 76.

7 **Cole, W F** and **Moorehead, D R.** High-strength calcium silicate hydrate: II. X-ray, DTA, chemical and electron miscroscope results. Autoclaved calcium silicate building products. The Society of Chemical Industry. London, 1967, p 135.

8 **Purton, M J.** The effect of sand grading on the calcium silicate brick reaction. Cement and Concrete Research, Vol 4, No 1, 1974, p 13.

9 **Kalousek, G L** and **Prebus, A F.** Crystal chemistry of hydrous calcium silicates: III Morphology and other properties of tobermorite and related phases. J. American Ceramic Society, Vol 41, 1958, p 124.

10 **Harker, R I.** Dehydration series in the system $CaSiO_3 - SiO_2 - H_2O$. J. American Ceramic Society, Vol 47, 1964, p 522.

11 **Lea, F M.** The Chemistry of Cement and Concrete, Edward Arnold, 1970, p 188.

Index

Where a topic is mentioned several times under the same heading only the first occurrence has normally been cited.

EDITOR'S NOTE

In addition to the Current Papers printed in full in the main body of this book, which covers the years 1973-1977, there are others in this broad subject area which for various reasons (such as, for example, their more localised appeal) have not been included. Their titles are, however, listed below for the benefit of any reader whose interests may extend to these areas.

17/72   Glass fibre reinforced cement
26/75   Fibre cement and concrete. A review
65/75   Pre-mixed glass fibre reinforced cement